English

The 11+
10-Minute Tests

For GL & other test providers

Ages
8-9

Practise • Prepare • Pass

Everything your child needs for 11+ success

How to use this book

This book is made up of 10-minute tests and puzzle pages.
There are answers and detailed explanations in the pull-out section at the back of the book.

10-Minute Tests

- There are 33 tests in this book, consisting of 17 comprehension texts worth 9 marks each, and 16 proofreading tests worth 16 marks each. Each test is a bite-sized version of a full length 11+ test, focusing on either the comprehension part or the proofreading part of the test.

- Each test is designed to cover a good range of the question styles and topics that your child could come across in their 11+ test.

- Your child should aim to score at least 8 out of 9 in each comprehension test and 14 out of 16 in each proofreading test. If they score less than this, use their results to work out the areas they need more practice on.

- If your child hasn't managed to finish the test in time, they need to work on increasing their speed, whereas if they have made a lot of mistakes, they need to work more carefully.

- Keep track of your child's scores using the progress chart on the inside back cover of the book.

Puzzle Pages

- There are 10 puzzle pages in this book. The puzzles are a great break from test preparation. They encourage children to practise the same skills that they will need in the test, but in a fun way.

Published by CGP

Editors:
Marc Barnard, Alex Fairer, Holly Robinson, James Summersgill

With thanks to Emma Cleasby and Judy Hornigold for the proofreading.
With thanks to Jan Greenway for the copyright research.

ISBN: 978 1 78294 772 1
Printed by Elanders Ltd, Newcastle upon Tyne
Clipart from Corel®

Based on the classic CGP style created by Richard Parsons.

Contents

Test 1: Comprehension

You have **10 minutes** to do this test. Work as quickly and accurately as you can.

Read this passage carefully and answer the questions that follow.

Noise in the Night

Anya lay in bed, staring at the moonlight shining through the gap in the curtains. Her eyes were refusing to close and her brain was refusing to rest. She was annoyed at Jordan and his scary stories because he knew how worked up she got over them. But he had a gift for storytelling. He was an expert at gradually building suspense
5 and then packing a powerful punch with a twist at the end. Although she knew it was all made up, she couldn't help but see Jordan's characters in every shadow and hear them in every noise.

She sighed, turning on to her side to stare at the wall. She and Jordan had spent all evening looking for his missing dog, Harvey. They felt as though they had left
10 no stone unturned, but still there was no sign of him. Harvey, a chocolate-coloured spaniel, was a hurricane of energy. Whether he was running after balls in the park or collecting sticks that were far too large for him to carry, he was never still. That afternoon, he had been pestering Jordan's mum while she was trying to do some gardening, and the next minute he was nowhere to be seen. This was quite
15 abnormal, because if Harvey wasn't getting under your feet, then he was probably getting under someone else's nearby.

Anya suddenly felt the skin prickle on her neck. A noise outside. She sat bolt upright in bed and froze, her eyes fixed on the curtains. It sounded like the back gate closing. Jordan's last story came flooding back into her mind. It had been
20 about a monster which came to your home in the dead of night, dragging his monstrous claws along the floor behind him as he made his way to your door. Her hands flew up to her mouth and she stifled a scream as she heard something being heaved along the paving stones towards the back door of her house. She dived over to the window and yanked back the curtains. But, instead of a nightmarish creature,
25 she saw Harvey dragging an oversized stick around the garden and the back gate banging in the breeze. Anya let out a huge sigh and fell back on her bed.

Answer these questions about the text. You can refer back to the text if you need to.

1. Why can't Anya sleep? Tick the box next to the correct answer.

    A   Her bed is uncomfortable.   ☐

    B   She can't stop thinking about Jordan's scary stories.   ☑

    C   The moon is too bright.   ☐

    D   Jordan is keeping her awake by telling her stories.   ☐

2. What does the phrase "left no stone unturned" (lines 9-10) mean?

    They've looked everywhere

3. Which of the following words best describes Harvey?
   Tick the box next to the correct answer.

    A   Energetic   ☑

    B   Obedient   ☐

    C   Lazy   ☐

    D   Scary   ☐

4. Which of the words below is closest in meaning to the word "abnormal" (line 15)?
   Tick the box next to the correct answer.

    A   Alarming   ☐

    B   Unusual   ☑

    C   Suspicious   ☐

    D   Mysterious   ☐

TURN OVER ➡

5. "Harvey wasn't getting under your feet" (line 15).
   Which of these words is a preposition?

   _____ *under* _____

6. Explain how Anya feels when she hears a "noise outside" (line 17).

   Panicked _____

7. Give another word or phrase that means the same as "dragging" (line 20) as it is used in the text.

   pulling _____

8. Explain how Anya feels when she sees Harvey in the garden.

   relieved _____

   _____

9. According to the passage, which of these statements is false?
   Tick the box next to the correct answer.

   A   Anya has an active imagination.   ☐

   B   The back gate to Anya's garden was left open.   ☐

   C   Jordan doesn't realise how scary Anya finds his stories. ☐

   D   Jordan's mum was one of the last people to see Harvey.   ☑

END OF TEST

/ 9

Test 2: Proofreading

You have **10 minutes** to do this test. Work as quickly and accurately as you can.

> This passage contains some spelling mistakes.
> Write the passage out again with the correct spellings.

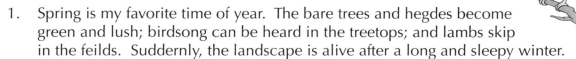

1. Spring is my favorite time of year. The bare trees and hegdes become green and lush; birdsong can be heard in the treetops; and lambs skip in the feilds. Suddernly, the landscape is alive after a long and sleepy winter.

Spring is my favourite time of year. The bare trees and hedges become green and lush; birdsongs canbeheard in the treetops; and lambs skip in the field. Suddenly, the landscape is alive after a long and sleepy winter.

> This passage has some punctuation mistakes.
> Write the passage out again with the correct punctuation.

2. I grabbed some biscuits from the shelf Put those back said Mum.

I grabbed some biscuits from the shelf. "Put ~~those~~ those back!" said Mum.

TURN OVER ➡

Choose the right word or phrase to complete the gap.
Circle the letter which matches the correct word.

3. We **made** **maker** **maked** **makes** **making** our way back down to the village.
    A   B   C   D   E

4. We **where** **wasn't** **were** **when** **was** weary from our long hike and
    A   B   C   D   E

5. **can't** **couldn't** **won't** **haven't** **shouldn't** wait to sit down in a cafe.
    A   B   C   D   E

6. We **find** **finding** **found** **finds** **founded** a nice looking one quite quickly
    A   B   C   D   E

7. and **sits** **sitting** **sit** **sat** **sitted** down at a picnic table outside in the shade.
    A   B   C D   E

8. I **lovings** **loving** **loves** **love** **lover** cafe stops after long hikes in the
    A   B   C   D   E

9. mountains. It **were** **is** **am** **are** **can** something to look forward to while you
    A   B   C D   E

are slowly trudging up a big steep hill and feeling tired. I looked eagerly at the menu

10. and **deciding** **decided** **decider** **decides** **decide** what to have.
    A   B   C   D   E

END OF TEST

/ 16

You have **10 minutes** to do this test. Work as quickly and accurately as you can.

Read this passage carefully and answer the questions that follow.

Isle of Skye

Despite its far-flung location, the Isle of Skye off the north-west coast of Scotland is one of the country's most popular tourist destinations. Its rolling moorlands, magnificent mountains and towering cliffs cast a spell over anyone who visits.

Skye is home to the Cuillin mountains, the most challenging peaks in Britain,
5 which makes it very popular amongst climbers and walkers. These sharp, craggy peaks soar dramatically from their surrounding landscape and are recognisable for miles around. They are heaven for the experienced climber, and some set themselves the task of climbing the entire 12km long Cuillin ridge in one go. This is incredibly tough and requires every last drop of fitness and concentration. As well
10 as impressive mountains, Skye is full of unusual scenery, such as the Old Man of Storr. The Old Man is a tall needle of rock which stands proudly on top of a hill.

Skye also has a certain magical quality which adds to its appeal. The island is full of myths and legends which have been handed down over centuries. One story would have us believe that the Old Man of Storr is the thumb of a giant buried in
15 the earth. Other places on Skye bear the name of fairies, such as the Fairy Pools and the Fairy Glen. The Fairy Glen is a beautiful area of small green hills and pools that looks so enchanting you could almost believe that fairies really do live there.

Although most tourists probably won't encounter a fairy on Skye, there's plenty of other wildlife to look out for, such as golden eagles, red deer and Atlantic salmon.

TURN OVER ➡

Answer these questions about the text. You can refer back to the text if you need to.

1. Explain what the phrase "far-flung location" (line 1) means.

   _____

2. "magnificent mountains" (line 3). What technique is this an example of? Tick the box next to the correct answer.

   A   Metaphor   ☐

   B   Simile   ☐

   C   Alliteration   ☐

   D   Rhyme   ☐

3. Skye is described as casting "a spell over anyone who visits" (line 3). What does this mean? Tick the box next to the correct answer.

   A   Tourists are fascinated by Skye.   ☐

   B   Tourists usually extend their visit to Skye.   ☐

   C   Tourists don't want to go on holiday anywhere else.   ☐

   D   A lot of witches live on Skye.   ☐

4. Explain why the Cuillin mountains are described as "heaven" (line 7) for climbers.

   _____

   _____

5. Find an adjective from the text that means the same as 'rocky'.

   _____

6. "This is incredibly tough and requires every last drop of fitness" (lines 8-9).
   Which of these words is an adverb? Tick the box next to the correct answer.

   A   incredibly   ☐

   B   tough   ☐

   C   fitness   ☐

   D   drop   ☐

7. What is the Old Man of Storr? Tick the box next to the correct answer.

   A   It is a mountain range.   ☐

   B   It is a cliff.   ☐

   C   It is a tall rock.   ☐

   D   It is a giant's thumb.   ☐

8. Explain how you think the Fairy Glen got its name.

   _____

   _____

9. Which of the words below is closest in meaning to the word "encounter"
   (line 18)? Tick the box next to the correct answer.

   A   Meet   ☐

   B   Visit   ☐

   C   Capture   ☐

   D   Identify   ☐

END OF TEST

/ 9

Time for a break! These puzzles are a great way to practise your **vocabulary** skills.

Dan's Den

Dan has given his friend instructions to find his secret den, but he has disguised the words in bold. Replace each of the bold words with a word that means the opposite to discover the directions to the den. Write the correct words on the lines.

Take the **wide** path through the woods. Go right at the first **crooked** tree. Cross the **deepest** part of the stream over the stepping stones. The den is straight ahead, to the left of a **sturdy** gate. Knock **rapidly** on the door five times.

Take the _____ path through the woods. Go right at the first _____ tree. Cross the _____ part of the stream over the stepping stones. The den is straight ahead, to the left of a _____ gate. Knock _____ on the door five times.

Synonym Scramble

Five words are hidden in the grid. Solve each anagram below then find its synonym in the wordsearch. Write the rearranged anagrams and the hidden words on the dashed lines below.

Example: i e u q t   q u i e t   h u s h e d

1. s r h u   _ _ _ _   _ _ _ _ _
2. e y h a v   _ _ _ _ _   _ _ _ _ _ _ _
3. m r s t a   _ _ _ _ _   _ _ _ _ _ _
4. u p o p r t s   _ _ _ _ _ _ _   _ _ _ _
5. t a c n r i e   _ _ _ _ _ _ _   _ _ _ _ _ _ _ _

P	O	S	I	T	I	V	E
Y	D	E	H	S	U	H	W
R	E	W	B	X	T	E	E
R	P	E	I	S	I	I	V
U	S	I	P	G	Z	V	E
H	P	L	H	N	T	E	R
A	E	T	R	E	M	S	L
H	Y	R	E	V	E	L	C

You have **10 minutes** to do this test. Work as quickly and accurately as you can.

> Choose the right word or phrase to complete the gap.
> Circle the letter which matches the correct word.

1. Sally **think thanks thinking thoughts thought** she saw her friend John in
    A   **B**   **C**   **D**   **E**

2. the crowd at the concert. She **catch caught catching catches catched**
                                     A   **B**   **C**   **D**   **E**

3. his eye, but John turned round as **an of when or though** he hadn't
                                        A **B** **C** **D** **E**

4. seen her. Sally was worried that he **will was might is should** still be
                                           A   **B**   **C**   **D**   **E**

    annoyed at her for going to the concert with Andrew instead of him.

> This passage has some spelling mistakes.
> Write the passage out again with the correct spellings.

5. That evening, my dad went to feed our cows and I joyned him. It always scairs me
    the way they come hertling towards us, but Dad's calmness always reasures me.

    _____

    _____

    _____

TURN OVER ➡

         Test 4

In each line there is one punctuation mistake. Circle the letter which matches the part of the sentence with the mistake.

6. "We'll be late for tea at Lauras' house if you don't hurry up!" shouted Mum.

    A   B   C   D   E

7. I feel like I have looked everywhere for my missing keys, but I still can't find them

    A   B   C   D   E

8. "I think we'd better ask for directions, said Clive, feeling lost and a bit foolish.

    A   B   C   D   E

9. John had an important football match Tomorrow and he was quite nervous about it.

    A   B   C   D   E

10. The new hotel has a car park, restaurant, swimming pool sauna and gym.

    A   B   C   D   E

11. "Do you know what the weather is going to be like at the weekend," asked Debs.

    A   B   C   D   E

12. Holly, one of my mums best friends, is taking her out for a fancy meal tonight.

    A   B   C   D   E

13. Karina, tasted some of the soup and couldn't decide if it needed more salt or not.

    A   B   C   D   E

END OF TEST

/ 16

Test 5: Comprehension

You have **10 minutes** to do this test. Work as quickly and accurately as you can.

Read this poem carefully and answer the questions that follow.

The Camel's Complaint

Canary-birds feed on sugar and seed,
Parrots have crackers to crunch;
And, as for the poodles, they tell me the noodles
Have chickens and cream for their lunch.
5 But there's never a question
About MY digestion —
Anything does for me!

Cats, you're aware, can repose* in a chair,
Chickens can roost upon rails;
10 Puppies are able to sleep in a stable,
And oysters can slumber in pails.
But no one supposes
A poor Camel dozes —
Any place does for me!

15 Lambs are enclosed where it's never exposed,
Coops are constructed for hens;
Kittens are treated to houses well heated,
And pigs are protected by pens.
But a Camel is handy
20 Wherever it's sandy —
Anywhere does for me!

People would laugh if you rode a giraffe,
Or mounted the back of an ox;
It's nobody's habit to ride on a rabbit,
25 Or try to bestraddle a fox.
But as for a Camel, he's
Ridden by families —
Any load does for me!

A snake is as round as a hole in the ground,
30 And weasels are wavy and sleek;
And no alligator could ever be straighter
Than lizards that live in a creek.
But a Camel's all lumpy
And bumpy and humpy —
35 Any shape does for me!"

Charles E. Carryl

*repose — *sleep*

Answer these questions about the text. You can refer back to the text if you need to.

1. Give another word or phrase that means the same as
    "crunch" (line 2) as it is used in the text.

_____

TURN OVER ➡

2. Where do the oysters in the poem sleep? Tick the box next to the correct answer.

   A In rivers ☐

   B In oceans ☐

   C In buckets ☐

   D In sinks ☐

3. "Lambs are enclosed where it's never exposed" (line 15). Explain what this line means in your own words.

   _____

   _____

4. Which of the following animal homes isn't mentioned in the poem? Tick the box next to the correct answer.

   A Kennel ☐

   B Stable ☐

   C Coop ☐

   D Pen ☐

5. According to the text, how would people react if they saw someone riding an ox? Tick the box next to the correct answer.

   A They would stop and stare. ☐

   B They would be confused. ☐

   C They would be surprised. ☐

   D They would find it funny. ☐

6. "A snake is as round as a hole in the ground" (line 29). What is this phrase an example of? Tick the box next to the correct answer.

A   Simile   ☐

B   Metaphor   ☐

C   Alliteration ☐

D   Adverbial   ☐

7. Find and copy a word from the poem that means the same as "glossy".

_____

8. "And no alligator could ever be straighter" (line 31).
   Which of these words is an adjective?

_____

9. What is the camel in the poem complaining about?
   Tick the box next to the correct answer.

A   That he's ugly compared to the other animals.   ☐

B   That he has to work in hot conditions.   ☐

C   That he isn't treated as well as other animals.   ☐

D   That the other animals think he isn't as good as them. ☐

END OF TEST

/ 9

You have **10 minutes** to do this test. Work as quickly and accurately as you can.

Read this passage carefully and answer the questions that follow.

Joss Naylor

Sometimes, incredible people and their achievements go unnoticed. One example is Joss Naylor, a sheep farmer from the Lake District. Among most people, his name means little, but in certain circles, he is celebrated as one of the finest mountain runners to have ever lived. To these people, he is known as 'Iron Joss'.

5 Joss lives and breathes mountains. Born in 1936, he has lived and farmed all his life in Wasdale, an area of the Lake District which has many mountains, including England's tallest, Scafell Pike. It shouldn't be much of a surprise, then, that Joss has an almost superhuman ability to run at speed over fells*. However, he wasn't always a fell runner. As a young man, he had such severe back problems that he

10 was advised to give up farming and had to spend time wearing a special corset. But, by the age of 24, he had had enough of being told to take it easy. He continued working, took up running, and when he ran his first fell race, discovered that he was a natural. All his time spent herding sheep on the fells had prepared him for this.

Joss's achievements are nothing short of legendary. For example, in 1975, he

15 smashed his own record of 63 peaks in 24 hours, completing a staggering 72. In 1986, at the age of 50, he ran up 214 fells in 7 days, 1 hour and 25 minutes. Many of his runs have raised money for charity, and he is a popular figure in the community. But it is fair to say that his fame does not reach far beyond the boundaries of the Lake District.

*fells — *mountains*

Answer these questions about the text. You can refer back to the text if you need to.

1. Write down a word or phrase from the text that means "overlooked".

_____

2. Why do you think some people refer to Joss as "Iron Joss" (line 4)?

_____

3. What does the word "superhuman" (line 8) mean?

   A   Incredible   ☐

   B   Terrifying   ☐

   C   Shocking   ☐

   D   Dangerous   ☐

4. "he had had enough of being told to take it easy" (line 11). What does this suggest about Joss's character? Tick the box next to the correct answer.

   A   He is reliable.   ☐

   B   He is determined.   ☐

   C   He is timid.   ☐

   D   He is lazy.   ☐

5. "race" (line 12) and "sheep" (line 13) as they are used in the text are examples of which type of word?

_____

TURN OVER ➡

6. "when he ran his first fell race" (line 12). Which of these words is a pronoun?
   Tick the box next to the correct answer.

   A   fell   ☐

   B   ran   ☐

   C   he   ☐

   D   when   ☐

7. Explain how Joss's way of life helped him to become a fell runner.

   _____

   _____

8. Which of the following statements is false? Tick the box next to the correct answer.

   A   Joss was in his twenties when he started fell running.   ☐

   B   Joss helps to raise money for charity.   ☐

   C   Joss gave up running when he was 24.   ☐

   D   Joss had health problems when he was younger.   ☐

9. Joss Naylor's fame "does not reach far beyond the boundaries of the Lake District"
   (lines 18-19). Explain what this means in your own words.

   _____

   _____

END OF TEST

/ 9

Puzzles 2

Time for a break! This puzzle will test your **personification**, **simile** and **metaphor** skills.

Coming to Life

Look at these pictures and describe each one using a metaphor, a simile or personification. The first one has been done for you.

The car coughed and spluttered.

_____

_____

_____

_____

_____

You have **10 minutes** to do this test. Work as quickly and accurately as you can.

Choose the right word or phrase to complete the gap.
Circle the letter which matches the correct word.

1. The school play **is do going will would** take place next Friday.
    A   B   C   D   E

2. There **are would will could shall** only a few tickets left, so make sure
    A   B   C   D   E

3. you **getting gets get got getted** one sooner rather than later to
    A   B   C   D   E

4. **avoiding avoids avoid avoided avoidance** disappointment.
    A   B   C   D   E

This passage has some punctuation mistakes.
Write the passage out again with the correct punctuation.

5. Last week I went to an art exhibition with my parents After we had walked around
    and seen everything we went for a meal at a Restaurant.

    _____

    _____

    _____

In each line there is one spelling mistake. Circle the letter which matches the part of the sentence with the mistake.

6. We could see a large hot air balloon above the hills in the distanse.

| A | B | C | D | E |

7. Tom carefully climed the tall, wobbly ladder to water the hanging baskets.

| A | B | C | D | E |

8. Marie really wanted to try ice skating because all of her frends had gone last week.

| A | B | C | D | E |

9. The hens all rushed towords me as I arrived with their favourite food.

| A | B | C | D | E |

10. Jo checked that no-one was coming and hid the broken ornerment behind the sofa.

| A | B | C | D | E |

11. I am amused by how long Max spends cleening and polishing his new bike.

| A | B | C | D | E |

12. Unicorns are magical horses with long poynty horns on top of their heads.

| A | B | C | D | E |

13. It was so warm that my ice cream melted befor I had a chance to eat it.

| A | B | C | D | E |

END OF TEST

/ 16

You have **10 minutes** to do this test. Work as quickly and accurately as you can.

Read this passage carefully and answer the questions that follow.

Sledging

I pressed my nose up against the window. Snow! Plump flakes were tumbling down and settling on top of the already thick white carpet below.

"Dad!" I yelled excitedly. "Dad, come here — look at all this snow!" He came shuffling in from the kitchen in his slippers.

5   "Yes, look at that," he said, peering over the top of his glasses. "It's coming down quite heavily isn't it, Lucy." He put his hand on my shoulder and looked down at me with a grin on his face. I looked back at him earnestly. "Well, I'm going back to read my paper," he said and started to turn away, his grin widening even further.

    "Oh, Dad," I said imploringly, grabbing his arm. "Please can we go sledging?
10 You said we would if we ever got snow."

    He ruffled my hair. "Of course we can. I know the perfect place. Go and get ready."

    Outside, the snow crunched delightfully beneath our feet. We were walking to a spot where my dad went sledging when he was a boy.

15   "Here we are then. I used to spend many a happy hour here with my sledge," said Dad. I stopped and looked around me.

    "This is it?" I asked, glancing at the slight incline that lay ahead of us.

    "It certainly is," said Dad. "My friends and I picked up some serious speed on here back in the day, let me tell you."

20   I wasn't convinced, but I pulled my sledge to the top of the incline anyway and got in. Dad gave me a push, and down I slid at a snail's pace. All I could hear behind me were his hoots of laughter.

    "OK, OK," he said, catching up to me and walking beside my sledge as it crawled along. "Maybe it isn't as steep as I remembered."

Answer these questions about the text. You can refer back to the text if you need to.

1. What does the word "Plump" (line 1) mean? Tick the box next to the right answer.

   A   Heavy   ☐

   B   Soft   ☐

   C   Fat   ☐

   D   White   ☐

2. "the already thick white carpet below" (line 2). What is this phrase an example of? Tick the box next to the right answer.

   A   Metaphor   ☐

   B   Alliteration   ☐

   C   Simile   ☐

   D   Onomatopoeia   ☐

3. How does Lucy feel when she sees the snow outside? Tick the box next to the right answer.

   A   Calm   ☐

   B   Delighted   ☐

   C   Unsure   ☐

   D   Annoyed   ☐

4. Why does Lucy grab her dad's arm (line 9)?

   _____

TURN OVER ➡

5. Explain in your own words how Lucy feels when she first sees the slope.

_____

_____

6. What does Lucy's dad mean by "back in the day" (line 19)?
   Tick the box next to the right answer.

   A   Yesterday   ☐

   B   At the end of the day   ☐

   C   Sometime in the past   ☐

   D   All day long   ☐

7. Write a word or phrase from the text which means "persuaded".

_____

8. Why does Lucy's dad laugh at her when she sledges down the hill?

_____

9. Which of these statements is false? Tick the box next to the right answer.

   A   Lucy's dad wears glasses.   ☐

   B   Lucy's dad went sledging when he was younger.   ☐

   C   Lucy's dad reads the newspaper.   ☐

   D   Lucy sledges down a steep hill.   ☐

END OF TEST

/ 9

You have **10 minutes** to do this test. Work as quickly and accurately as you can.

This passage contains some spelling mistakes.
Write the passage out again with the correct spellings.

1.   I went to the kichen to make a cup of tea. To my suprise, there was a bird flying arownd in there. It must have flown in threw the window.

_____

_____

_____

This passage has some punctuation mistakes.
Write the passage out again with the correct punctuation.

2.   My mum has always wanted to go to egypt, so we are taking her. as a present for her Birthday. Shes going to love it!

_____

_____

_____

TURN OVER ➡

25

Choose the right word or phrase to complete the gap.
Circle the letter which matches the correct word.

3. Simon **am was are were be** jealous of people who had musical ability. He
        A   B   C   D   E

4. **longing longer longs long longed** to be able to patter away effortlessly on the
        A   B   C   D   E

5. keys of a piano or pluck at the strings of a guitar **have with has these his**
                                                             A   B   C   D   E

6. nimble fingers. Sadly, **he his she they him** just wasn't very musically gifted.
                              A   B   C   D   E

7. He had tried music lessons with **countless several many lots various** of
                                        A   B   C   D   E

8. different tutors, and **those them they're there their** winces at his screechy
                           A   B   C   D   E

9. violin playing or his tuneless singing **do is did had does** nothing to put him
                                            A   B   C   D   E

    off. Simon's tutors liked his determination though and suggested that he try

10. something **simply easily easier simplest ease** to play, like the tambourine.
                A   B   C   D   E

END OF TEST

/ 16

Time for a break! This puzzle is a great way to practise your **word-making** skills.

Letter Ladders

Make your way down the ladders by changing the words at the top by one letter at a time. Use the clues to the right of each ladder to help you find each missing word. When you have filled in the ladders, unscramble the letters in the white squares to find a hidden word which has a similar meaning to 'climb'.

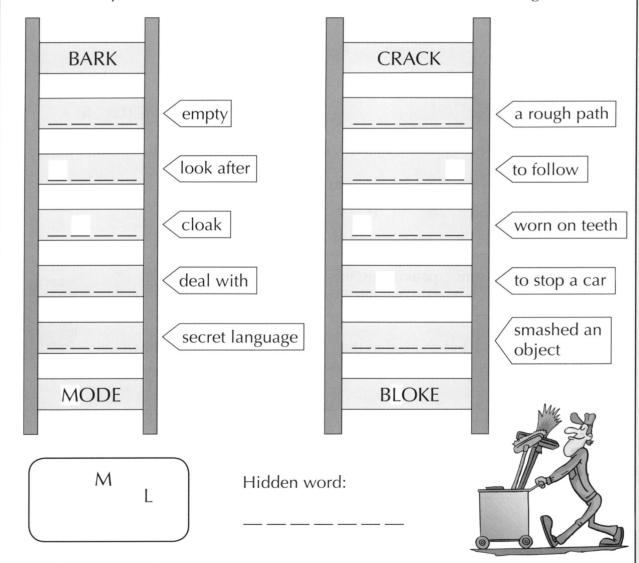

BARK

_ _ _ _ _ < empty

▢ _ _ _ < look after

_ ▢ _ _ < cloak

_ _ _ _ < deal with

_ _ _ _ < secret language

MODE

CRACK

_ _ _ _ _ < a rough path

_ _ _ ▢ _ < to follow

▢ _ _ _ _ < worn on teeth

_ ▢ _ _ _ < to stop a car

_ _ _ _ _ < smashed an object

BLOKE

M _ _ _ L

Hidden word:

_ _ _ _ _ _ _

You have **10 minutes** to do this test. Work as quickly and accurately as you can.

> Choose the right word or phrase to complete the gap.
> Circle the letter which matches the correct word.

1. Ant walked to the end of his driveway and looked for **all any an every few**
                         A **B** **C** **D** **E**

2. sign of the red van. He **have were had has was** been waiting for the post
               A **B** **C** **D** **E**

3. all morning. The postman was never usually **the bit then much this** late.
                  A **B** **C** **D** **E**

Ant's friend, Shelley, had sent him something in the mail and he couldn't wait to

4. see what it **were are be is was**.
          A **B** **C** **D** **E**

> This passage has some spelling mistakes.
> Write the passage out again with the correct spellings.

5. The trees groned and creaked as their brantches swayed in the howling
    wind. Bats flew hear and there and somewhere, an owl loadly hooted.

_____

_____

_____

In each line there is one punctuation mistake. Circle the letter which matches the part of the sentence with the mistake.

6.   I would love to visit New Zealand, Iceland America and Norway.

         A   B   C   D   E

7.   Let's go and get a drink at that café," he said over the chatter of the noisy crowd.

         A   B   C   D   E

8.   "How much of this pasta do you think I should put in the pan!" asked Josh.

         A   B   C   D   E

9.   My gran could'nt stand untidiness, so her house was always incredibly clean.

         A   B   C   D   E

10.   My friend Toby is convinced that he saw a spaceship in the sky, the other night.

         A   B   C   D   E

11.   Kate and susie are going with their parents to Cornwall in the summer.

         A   B   C   D   E

12.   "I'd like to plant my own vegetable patch in the garden," said Harry to his mum."

         A   B   C   D   E

13.   Nasreen forgot to fill her dogs bowl with food before she went out.

         A   B   C   D   E

END OF TEST

/ 16

You have **10 minutes** to do this test. Work as quickly and accurately as you can.

Read this poem carefully and answer the questions that follow.

The Travellers and the Purse

Two friends once were walking in sociable chat,
When one spied a purse on the ground;
"Oh, see!" said he, (thank my fortune for that),
"What a large sum of money I've found!"

5 "No, do not say I," said his friend, "for you know
That you should share it with me."
"I share it with you?" said the other. "How so?
He who found it the owner should be."

"Be it so," said his friend, "but what is that I hear?
10 "Stop thief!" one is calling to you;
He comes with a policeman close in the rear!"
Said the other, "Oh, what shall we do?"

"No, do not say we," said his friend, "for you know
You claimed the sole right to the prize!
15 And since all the money was taken by you,
With you the problem lies."

Marmaduke Park

Answer these questions about the text. You can refer back to the text if you need to.

1. What were the travellers doing when they found the purse?

_____

30

2. Which of the words below is closest in meaning to the word "spied" (line 2)?
Tick the box next to the correct answer.

   A   Tracked   ☐

   B   Revealed   ☐

   C   Spotted   ☐

   D   Looked   ☐

3. How does the traveller feel when he finds the purse?
Tick the box next to the correct answer.

   A   Relieved   ☐

   B   Shaken   ☐

   C   Confused   ☐

   D   Thankful   ☐

4. "What a large sum of money I've found!" (line 4).
Which of these words is an adjective?

_____

5. Why might the other traveller think that the money should be shared?

_____

_____

TURN OVER ➡

6. Which of these words best describes the friend who finds the money?
   Tick the box next to the correct answer.

   A   Cunning   ☐

   B   Brave   ☐

   C   Selfish   ☐

   D   Cruel   ☐

7. Explain what happens in the third verse.

   _____

   _____

8. What type of word are "claimed" (line 14) and "taken" (line 15)?
   Tick the box next to the correct answer.

   A   Adverb   ☐

   B   Verb   ☐

   C   Noun   ☐

   D   Adjective   ☐

9. What do you think the moral of the poem is?
   Tick the box next to the correct answer.

   A   Share good luck with friends and they will help you through bad times.   ☐

   B   Bad luck is a true test of friendship.   ☐

   C   Do not take advantage of your friends.   ☐

   D   It's better to have no friends at all than to have a greedy one.   ☐

END OF TEST

/ 9

Test 12: Proofreading

You have **10 minutes** to do this test. Work as quickly and accurately as you can.

> Choose the right word or phrase to complete the gap.
> Circle the letter which matches the correct word.

1. As I was walking **next   close   along   between   among** the beach, I spotted
                 A   **B**   **C**   **D**   **E**

2. Ted's ice cream van **upon   around   on   in   over** the distance. There was a
                 A   **B**   **C** **D**   **E**

   large queue, but I was desperate to get there before he drove away, so I broke into

3. a run. He sold the **nice   tasty   excellent   delicious   best** ice cream I'd ever
                 A   **B**   **C**   **D**   **E**

4. tasted and had **many   lots   most   all   some** of unusual flavours.
                 A **B** **C** **D** **E**

> This passage has some punctuation mistakes.
> Write the passage out again with the correct punctuation.

5. I think itd be really great to have a pet dragon. They can fly breathe fire
   and theyre really fierce. No-one would bother you, if you had a pet dragon.

   _____

   _____

   _____

TURN OVER ➡

          33

In each line there is one spelling mistake. Circle the letter which matches the part of the sentence with the mistake.

6. When we finally made it to the top of the mountain there wasn't a breth of wind.

    A   B   C   D   E

7. The castle will be shut for two munths while parts of it are being repaired.

    A   B   C   D   E

8. A red squirrel ran out onto the rode in front of me while I was cycling yesterday.

    A   B   C   D   E

9. I visitted my aunty on her farm last week and stroked a couple of tiny lambs.

    A   B   C   D   E

10. Tom made tea as a surprise for his parents last night, but he burnt almost evrything.

    A   B   C   D   E

11. My dad is trying to cut down on the amount of cofee that he drinks every day.

    A   B   C   D   E

12. Sam is organising a berthday meal for Jensen next Tuesday if you would like to come.

    A   B   C   D   E

13. Lola and four of her friends are having a picnic tonight on the shaw of the lake.

    A   B   C   D   E

END OF TEST

/ 16

Puzzles 4

Time for a break! These puzzles are a great way to practise your **vocabulary** skills.

Cross Word

Mr. Ross is very cross. The words in the box below are synonyms for how he's feeling. Fit the words into the grid then write the letters in the grey squares in the empty box. Rearrange these letters to find out why Mr. Ross is so cross.

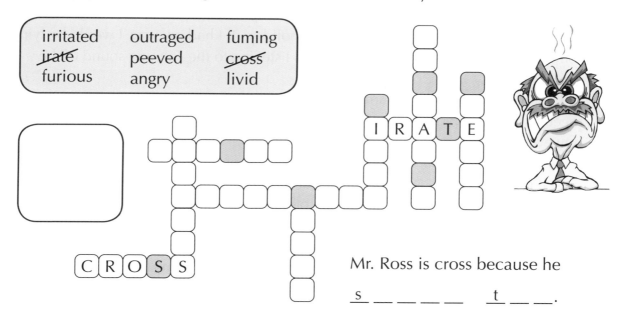

irritated outraged fuming
~~irate~~ peeved ~~cross~~
furious angry livid

I R A T E

C R O S S

Mr. Ross is cross because he

s _ _ _ _ _   t _ _.

Verb Picking

Circle the verbs on the tree.
The bold letters in the verbs can be rearranged to spell another verb.

The verb made from the letters in bold is

_____

write **wonderful** follow
am**u**se history
grab
never **invent** ho**p**e
somewhere **hatred**

You have **10 minutes** to do this test. Work as quickly and accurately as you can.

Read this passage carefully and answer the questions that follow.

Family Holiday

I carried on plodding through the sea of green and everything looked the same. I dragged my feet heavily and blew air out of my cheeks. This was dull. It was definitely not how I wanted to spend this holiday. If I had my way, I would be lying somewhere sandy, soaking up the sun and listening to the calming sound of the
5 waves.

I enjoy holidays with my family. I really do. It's great to spend quality time together and to explore somewhere you've never been before. What I don't enjoy, however, is being dragged to see big gardens. Yes, I appreciate that might be an impressive tree and that might be a very rare type of plant, but I just can't bring
10 myself to care. At all. I could see my parents up ahead fussing over different flowers and eagerly pointing things out to each other. I sighed.

Finally, we made it out of the garden and into the gift shop. In my view, this was the only tolerable part of the entire experience. Mum always ends up buying some kind of plant though. Sure enough, long after I had lost interest and gone to wait by
15 the car, Mum came staggering out, barely visible behind a pile of red leaves.

"You can never have too many plants," she grunted as she tried to heave the monstrous thing into the boot.

"I think you can, Mum," I said, helping her wrestle it inside. "I don't know how you find room for them all. We'll have to start charging people to walk round our
20 garden at this rate."

"That's a good idea," she said, giving me a playful nudge. "You can be a tour guide." I scowled and got inside the car.

Answer these questions about the text. You can refer back to the text if you need to.

1. Which word best describes how the narrator is feeling in the first paragraph?
   Tick the box next to the correct answer.

   A   Alert   ☐

   B   Relaxed   ☐

   C   Tired   ☐

   D   Bored   ☐

2. "heavily" (line 2) and "definitely" (line 3) are examples of which part of speech?
   Tick the box next to the correct answer.

   A   Verb   ☐

   B   Adverb   ☐

   C   Adjective   ☐

   D   Noun   ☐

3. How would the narrator prefer to spend her holiday?

   _____

4. Which of the words below is closest in meaning to the word "impressive" (line 9)?
   Tick the box next to the correct answer.

   A   Unique   ☐

   B   Old   ☐

   C   Remarkable   ☐

   D   Tall   ☐

TURN OVER ➡

5. Give another word or phrase that means the same as "type" (line 9) as it is used in the text.

_____

6. How can you tell the narrator's parents like gardens?

_____

_____

7. What part of visiting the garden did the narrator actually enjoy?

_____

8. Which of the following phrases best describes the plant the narrator's mum buys? Tick the box next to the correct answer.

    A   Fragrant and flowery ☐

    B   Large and leafy ☐

    C   Bushy and green ☐

    D   Small and red ☐

9. Explain how the narrator feels in lines 21-22.

_____

_____

END OF TEST

/ 9

Test 14: Proofreading

You have **10 minutes** to do this test. Work as quickly and accurately as you can.

This passage contains some spelling mistakes.
Write the passage out again with the correct spellings.

1. My grandfather has won first prize for his gardern in the local competishion. He came second last year, so he is realy pleased. We are going with him on Saterday to collect his winnings.

_____

_____

_____

_____

This passage has some punctuation mistakes.
Write the passage out again with the correct punctuation.

2. Lucys cat, bilbo, has got himself stuck up a tree again. Her mum dad and brother are all outside trying to coax it down, but it isnt working.

_____

_____

_____

TURN OVER ➡

Choose the right word or phrase to complete the gap.
Circle the letter which matches the correct word.

3. My gran quite **daily** **always** **often** **sometimes** **normally** gives me lifts to school.
                A   B   C   D   E

4. She drives very **slowed** **slowly** **slower** **slows** **slowing** and it is embarrassing
             A   B   C   D   E

5. when the cars **behind** **rear** **back** **after** **next** start beeping at us. It turns out that
           A   B   C   D   E

6. people are quite impatient when it comes to **did** **doer** **does** **do** **doing** the
                                                     A   B   C   D   E

7. school run. Gran has good taste **of** **in** **about** **on** **with** music though, which
                                    A   B   C   D   E

8. makes up for it. I enjoy **arrived** **arriver** **arrives** **arriving** **arrive** at the school
                     A   B   C   D   E

   gates with the windows down and heavy metal music blaring, my gran

9. **nod** **nods** **nodded** **nodding** **noddy** her head along to it. The looks on my friends'
     A   B   C   D   E

10. faces are **funny** **hilarity** **amuse** **entertain** **enjoyment** to see.
           A   B   C   D   E

END OF TEST

/ 16

You have **10 minutes** to do this test. Work as quickly and accurately as you can.

Read this passage carefully and answer the questions that follow.

Polar Bears

Polar bears live in the most northern part of the world, the Arctic Circle. The Arctic is a huge mass of ice and glaciers, most of which stays frozen all year. The climate is extremely harsh, with bitter, high-speed winds and temperatures that fall to as low as −40°C, meaning it is almost impossible for humans and most other
5 species to live there. The polar bear, however, can survive such tough conditions because it has a thick coat of white fur, which protects it from the cold.

Although the African bush elephant is the world's largest land mammal, the polar bear claims the title of being the world's largest carnivorous (meat-eating) land mammal. Polar bears are often thought of as big, cuddly teddy bears, due to
10 their thick, white coats and gentle eyes. However, it would be foolish to give them a hug. They can weigh up to 700 kg (almost ten times as much as the average human), meaning they are extraordinarily strong. Their incredible strength, as well as their thick, padded paws and razor-sharp teeth, means that polar bears are fearsome predators on the ice.

15 Their diet consists mainly of seals. Seals have a large amount of blubber, a thick layer of fat, which keeps the polar bear warm after it has consumed it. Occasionally, polar bears can find hunting difficult if there are too few animals in the area for them to eat. Polar bears are very independent and can sometimes travel thousands of miles alone, scouring and scavenging for food.

TURN OVER ➡

Test 15

Answer these questions about the text. You can refer back to the text if you need to.

1. "The climate is extremely harsh" (lines 2-3).
   Which of these words is an adjective? Tick the box next to the correct answer.

   A   climate   ☐

   B   extremely   ☐

   C   harsh   ☐

   D   is   ☐

2. Give one reason why humans would struggle to live in the Arctic Circle.

   _____

3. Which word best describes polar bears?
   Tick the box next to the correct answer.

   A   Curious   ☐

   B   Powerful   ☐

   C   Angry   ☐

   D   Lonely   ☐

4. Explain why polar bears are described as "fearsome predators" (line 14).

   _____

   _____

5. Give another word or phrase that means the same as "consumed" (line 16)
   as it used in the text.

   _____

6. Which of the following statements is false? Tick the box next to the correct answer.

    A   Polar bears are heavier than humans.   ☐

    B   A polar bear's fur stops it from getting cold.   ☐

    C   Polar bears eat seals.   ☐

    D   It is always easy for polar bears to find food.   ☐

7. "climate" (line 2) and "predators" (line 14) as they are used in the text are examples of which type of word? Tick the box next to the correct answer.

    A   Adverb   ☐

    B   Noun   ☐

    C   Preposition   ☐

    D   Adjective   ☐

8. Give one reason why seals are a good source of food for polar bears.

    _____

    _____

9. Polar bears will sometimes travel thousands of miles to...
    Tick the box next to the correct answer.

    A   search for a partner.   ☐

    B   look for food.   ☐

    C   escape the cold.   ☐

    D   escape hunters.   ☐

END OF TEST

/ 9

Have a go at these puzzles to test your knowledge of **conjunctions**.

Conjunction Creek

You're about to take a trip down Conjunction Creek, but it's risky.

You need to take all the boxes labelled with conjunctions from your camp with you to make sure you have a safe trip. Circle all the **conjunctions** you need to put into your canoe — but don't take anything else or you might sink...

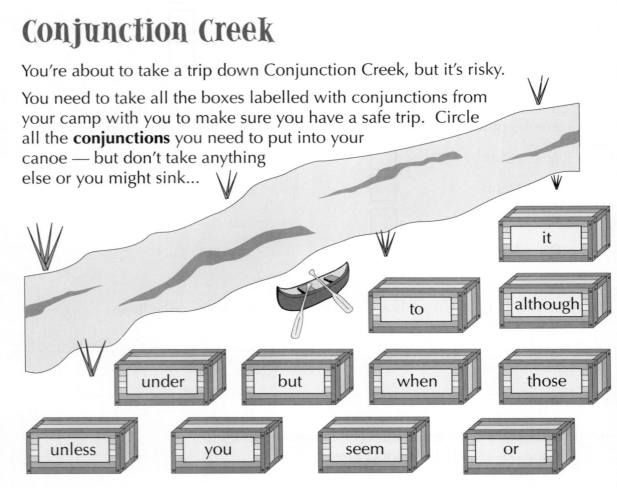

River Rapids

It looks like you've just got caught in some fast-flowing rapids. Use an appropriate **subordinating conjunction** to complete each of the following sentences to paddle your way out.

1. I only go canoeing in the summer .... the weather is hotter.

2. .... the rapids were strong, Charlotte managed to paddle.

Test 16: Proofreading

You have **10 minutes** to do this test. Work as quickly and accurately as you can.

> Choose the right word or phrase to complete the gap.
> Circle the letter which matches the correct word.

1. Yesterday, Sam accidentally **breaking** **breaks** **break** **broke** **breaked** his sister's
                    A   **B**   **C**   **D**   **E**

2. favourite mug. He knew she would be **furious** **anger** **annoy** **upsets** **irritate**
                    A   **B**   **C**   **D**   **E**

3. with him, so he **buying** **buy** **bought** **buyed** **buys** an identical
               A   **B**   **C**   **D**   **E**

4. one. She hasn't realised, **for** **but** **yet** **as** **so** Sam is very pleased with himself.
            A **B** **C** **D** **E**

> This passage has some spelling mistakes.
> Write the passage out again with the correct spellings.

5. The bakary in town makes the best pies I have ever taysted. I usualy buy one for
    myself every Saturday morning and take home a couple for my pairents.

    _____

    _____

    _____

TURN OVER ➡

Test 16

In each line there is one punctuation mistake. Circle the letter which matches the part of the sentence with the mistake.

6. The brightly painted house's on the street behind us are lovely and full of character.

       A   **B**   **C**   **D**   **E**

7. "Can you dry the pots after I've washed them"? asked Marc, turning on the tap.

       A   **B**   **C**   **D**   **E**

8. Next Thursday, a mayor will open the new village Hall in an official ceremony.

       A   **B**   **C**   **D**   **E**

9. "I can't find your dad's missing wallet anywhere in the house, sighed Mum.

       A   **B**   **C**   **D**   **E**

10. As a surprise for her sister, Jenna has bought her concert tickets, and a new bag.

        A   **B**   **C**   **D**   **E**

11. "i can't believe there is only one chocolate biscuit left in the tin," complained Max.

        A   **B**   **C**   **D**   **E**

12. "Would you like to come round to my house after school to have tea," asked Marie.

        A   **B**   **C**   **D**   **E**

13. Paul and Jacks idea to throw water bombs at their dad resulted in a big telling off.

        A   **B**   **C**   **D**   **E**

END OF TEST

/ 16

You have **10 minutes** to do this test. Work as quickly and accurately as you can.

Read this passage carefully and answer the questions that follow.

Grace Darling

On a small rocky island off the northeast coast of England, there is a lighthouse.
A man named William Darling was once keeper of this lighthouse and his daughter,
Grace, lived with him. Every day, Grace Darling helped her father to turn on the
lights that warned sailors to steer their ships away from the dangerous rocks, which
5 otherwise would smash them to pieces.

One stormy night, Grace woke with the sound of screams in her ears. The
screams came from the sea, so she knew that a ship must be in distress. She woke
her father, but they could see nothing in the darkness. When daylight came, they
found that a ship had been wrecked upon the rocks some way off, and a few people
10 were clinging to the masts. Grace wished to go at once in a boat to save them. At
first, her father hung back, for the wind and sea were wild, and he feared that the
small boat would be overturned by the great waves. Then Grace ran to the boat, and
seized an oar, because she could not bear to let the poor men die without trying to
save them. The father could not let his brave daughter go alone, so he followed, and
15 they rowed off.

It was hard work pulling against the strong sea, and several times the small boat
was almost sunk. But at last it reached the wreck, and William Darling managed to
land upon the rock, and with great care and skill helped the half-frozen people into
the small boat. Then they were taken to the lighthouse, where Grace warmed and
20 fed them until the storm ceased and they could return to their homes.

Answer these questions about the text. You can refer back to the text if you need to.

1. In which country is the lighthouse from the text located?

_____

2. Which of these statements is true? Tick the box next to the correct answer.

    A   William Darling lived alone. ☐

    B   Grace Darling worked alone at the lighthouse. ☐

    C   The lighthouse was dangerous to sailors. ☐

    D   The lighthouse was located on an island. ☐

3. Give another word or phrase that means the same as "distress" (line 7)
    as it is used in the text.

    _____

4. "they could see nothing in the darkness" (line 8).
    Which word in this phrase is a preposition?

    _____

5. What did the father and daughter find when daylight came?
    Tick the box next to the correct answer.

    A   A sailor called William Darling ☐

    B   A ship that had crashed into the rocks ☐

    C   A rocky island ☐

    D   Some dangerous rocks ☐

6. Which of the following words best describes the sea in the text?
   Tick the box next to the correct answer.

   A   Fierce   ☐

   B   Calm   ☐

   C   Shallow   ☐

   D   Warm   ☐

7. What does the phrase "at once" (line 10) mean?

   _____

8. Why did the father not want to go in the boat with his daughter at first?

   _____

9. How did Grace help the victims of the shipwreck after she rescued them from the
   sea? Tick the box next to the correct answer.

   A   She gave them some money.   ☐

   B   She gave them a place to sleep.   ☐

   C   She gave them a new boat.   ☐

   D   She gave them something to eat.   ☐

END OF TEST

/ 9

You have **10 minutes** to do this test. Work as quickly and accurately as you can.

Choose the right word or phrase to complete the gap.
Circle the letter which matches the correct word.

1.   Alan **keep   kepped   keeped   keeping   kept** asking Mike to clean his car
            A   B   C   D   E

2.   for him because it **were   be   was   are   will** dirty. Alan was very busy at
                          A   B   C   D   E

3.   work and would **of   be   have   a   if** cleaned his car himself if he'd had
                       A   B   C   D   E

4.   more time. Mike was also very busy, but he offered **him   and   that   to   too**
                                                            A   B   C   D   E

     clean the car anyway.

This passage has some punctuation mistakes.
Write the passage out again with the correct punctuation.

5.   Hello, Officer said the young man. "Do you know what the time is."

     _____

     _____

     _____

50

In each line there is one spelling mistake. Circle the letter which matches the part of the sentence with the mistake.

6. After three weeks and not a drop of rain, the grownd was utterly parched.

   A   B   C   D   E

7. Neeling down, Desmond carefully looped each shoelace around the other.

   A   B   C   D   E

8. The paper plane swooped and plunged in the summer breeze like a berd.

   A   B   C   D   E

9. Once Timmy started to run, he kept runing until he got home.

   A   B   C   D   E

10. Countless hours after the mechanic started repairing it, the car splutered into life.

   A   B   C   D   E

11. Buster picked up an aword for being the most obedient dog at the show.

   A   B   C   D   E

12. He carefully epproached the islanders, who looked at him and grinned wickedly.

   A   B   C   D   E

13. It was the most beautiful peace of music that Matt had ever heard.

   A   B   C   D   E

END OF TEST

/ 16

Test 18

Time for a break! This puzzle is a great way to practise your **logic** skills.

PC Plod's Perplexing Cryptogram

PC Plod has a funny joke to tell you, but he's written it in code.

Each blank line below has a number underneath it which corresponds to a letter. Some letters have already been solved. Not all letters appear in the joke.

Using all of your detective skills, try to crack this police joke by filling in the blanks.

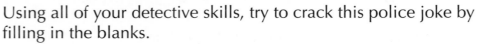

A	B	C	D	E	F	G	H	I	J	K	L	M	N	O	P	Q	R	S	T	U	V	W	X	Y	Z
			13		8	26				15	1	12			3		19		17						

_ / p _ l _ _ _ m _ _ / _ p _ t _ / _ / _ _ m _ _ / d r _ _ _ _ g /
5   3 25 1 20 22 9 12 5 6   24 3 25 17 24   5   10 25 12 5 6   13 19 20 23 20 6 8

_ _ d / k _ _ t t _ _ g / _ t / t h _ / _ _ m _ / t _ m _.
5 6 13   15 6 20 17 17 20 6 8   5 17   17 26 9   24 5 12 9   17 20 12 9

D r _ _ _ _ g / _ p / _ _ _ _ d _ / h _ r, / h _ / _ h _ _ t _ ...
13 19 20 23 20 6 8   2 3   7 9 24 20 13 9   26 9 19   26 9   24 26 25 2 17 24

"P _ l l / _ _ _ r!"
3 2 1 1   25 23 9 19

"_ _," / _ h _ / _ h _ _ t _ / _ _ _ k, / "_ / p _ _ r / _ _ / _ _ _ k _!"
6 25   24 26 9   24 26 25 2 17 24   7 5 22 15   5   3 5 20 19   25 21   24 25 22 15 24

You have **10 minutes** to do this test. Work as quickly and accurately as you can.

Read this poem carefully and answer the questions that follow.

The Trouble with Tadfink

Tadfink stared, rather taken aback,
The leaves were smoking, the branches black.
Where his home used to be,
Was a pile of ash, no longer a tree.

5 Other gnomes gathered for a peek,
Silent until one dared to speak.
"Elven magic?" a little gnome guessed.
"A fungus!" "A curse!" cried the rest.

The throng broke out into rowdy chatter.
10 How would they ever solve the matter?
"Will our homes be next?" the crowd all feared.
Tadfink paused and stroked his beard.

He climbed upon a sizeable rock,
And faced the crowd, which was still in shock.
15 He cleared his throat and began to speak,
"Has anyone seen anything odd this week?"

One gnome stepped forward, and to this he said:
"Last night, I saw a flash of red,
Smoke it billowed and embers glowed,
20 And it all engulfed Tadfink's abode."

Tadfink sighed, "I've been a bit daft.
Please don't tut, and please don't laugh.
I left my stove on," he said in disgust.
"My oatmeal cookies turned my house to dust!"

TURN OVER

            Test 19

1. Give another word or phrase that means the same as "taken aback" (line 1) as it is used in the text.

    _____

2. Which of the following words describes how the gnomes are feeling in line 5? Tick the box next to the correct answer.

    A Curious ☐

    B Angry ☐

    C Unhappy ☐

    D Carefree ☐

3. What does the phrase "rowdy chatter" (line 9) suggest about how the gnomes are behaving?

    _____

4. "How would they ever solve the matter?" (line 10). Which word in this phrase is a pronoun?

    _____

5. Which of these statements is false? Tick the box next to the correct answer.

    A The gnomes are worried their houses will be damaged. ☐

    B Tadfink speaks to a crowd of gnomes. ☐

    C Tadfink stands on a small rock. ☐

    D Tadfink has a beard. ☐

54

6.   Find a word from the text which means the same as "strange".

_____

7.   "Last night, I saw a flash of red" (line 18).
     Which word in this phrase is a verb?

_____

8.   What was it that damaged the tree?
     Tick the box next to the correct answer.

     A   A fungus   ☐

     B   A curse   ☐

     C   An evil spell   ☐

     D   Tadfink's oven   ☐

9.   Explain how Tadfink feels at the end of the poem.

_____

END OF TEST

/ 9

You have **10 minutes** to do this test. Work as quickly and accurately as you can.

Read this passage carefully and answer the questions that follow.

The History of the Piano

Since the eighteenth century, the pianoforte (now simply known as the piano) has been the instrument of choice for many composers and musicians. But the piano hasn't always looked as it does today — it has undergone several changes over the years.

5   Instruments that make sounds when keys are pressed were used by the ancient Greeks. However, stringed keyboard instruments became more popular in Europe in the fourteenth and fifteenth centuries. The most famous of these instruments was the harpsichord. The harpsichord looks very similar in shape to a modern grand piano, but it creates sound in a very different way.

10 Harpsichords contain lots of small points called 'plectra', which, when a key is pressed, pluck a string to produce a note.

    The modern piano was invented by an Italian, Bartolomeo Cristofori, around the year 1700. Cristofori was an expert harpsichord maker who wanted to improve this instrument. He created an instrument that used hammers instead

15 of 'plectra' to strike a string. Whereas notes on the harpsichord are always produced at the same volume, Cristofori's design meant that the musician could play a note either softly or loudly. This is where the piano got its name — *pianoforte* means 'soft and loud' in Italian.

    Cristofori's instrument was hugely popular with musicians of the time,

20 and the piano gradually replaced the harpsichord, which was used a lot less frequently by the nineteenth century.

Answer these questions about the text. You can refer back to the text if you need to.

1.   Give another name for the piano.

_____

2. When did the piano start to become popular with musicians?
Tick the box next to the correct answer.

A   During the era of the ancient Greeks   ☐

B   In the fourteenth century   ☐

C   In the fifteenth century   ☐

D   In the eighteenth century   ☐

3. What does the word "several" mean in line 3?

_____

4. The 'plectra' in a harpsichord are...
Tick the box next to the correct answer.

A   strings.   ☐

B   keys.   ☐

C   small points.   ☐

D   the notes it makes.   ☐

5. "Cristofori was an expert harpsichord maker" (line 13).
Which word in this phrase is a determiner?

_____

TURN OVER ➡

6. Which of the following words best describes Bartolomeo Cristofori?
Tick the box next to the correct answer.

A Unusual   ☐

B Serious   ☐

C Rich   ☐

D Skilled   ☐

7. Give another word or phrase that means the same as "produced" (line 16) as it is used in the text.

_____

8. Explain what happened to the popularity of the harpsichord after the invention of the piano.

_____

_____

9. According to the passage, which of these statements is false?

A The piano was invented by an Italian.   ☐

B The harpsichord has a similar shape to the piano.   ☐

C Harpsichords and pianos produce sound in the same way.   ☐

D Notes made by a harpsichord are always at the same volume.   ☐

END OF TEST

/ 9

You have **10 minutes** to do this test. Work as quickly and accurately as you can.

> This passage contains some spelling mistakes.
> Write the passage out again with the correct spellings.

1. Joan shuffled towards the balkony. The sent of woodsmoke filled the air. The smell remineded Joan of the farm, cauzing her to become even more homesick.

_____

_____

_____

> This passage has some punctuation mistakes.
> Write the passage out again with the correct punctuation.

2. Suddenly, johns eyes grew heavy. After hauling himself onto the sofa he lay down. It wasnt long before he fell into a deep sleep.

_____

_____

_____

TURN OVER ➡

Choose the right word or phrase to complete the gap.
Circle the letter which matches the correct word.

3. Tom and Jacob **climbs** **clamb** **climbed** **clomb** **climed** up onto the tallest

    A   B   C   D   E

4. branch. They were high up — **more** **very** **so** **bit** **much** higher than they

    A   B   C   D   E

5. had ever been before — which **make** **maked** **makes** **made** **making** them feel

    A   B   C   D   E

6. very queasy. **Looking** **Look** **Looks** **Looked** **Lookes** around the tree,

    A   B   C   D   E

7. Jacob spotted something. There **were** **was** **would** **will** **be** a small hole in

    A   B   C   D   E

8. the trunk, and he thought he **can't** **will** **could** **should** **would** hear tweeting

    A   B   C   D   E

9. sounds coming from it. He peered in to **takes** **taken** **taking** **took** **take** a look

    A   B   C   D   E

10. and saw a nest of baby birds, squawking frantically **of** **in** **for** **before** **instead**

    A B C   D   E

    their mother.

END OF TEST

/ 16

Another test done — time for a little treat. Here's another puzzle to have a go at...

King Pat's Dingbats

King Pat wants to find his cleverest knights to send on a secret quest, so he's given them a series of puzzles to solve. The answers to all of the puzzles are common sayings.

King Pat's tip to his knights is 'say what you see'. Write the answers on the lines below.

1.

Think

_____

_____

2.

beans beans beans
beans beans beans
beans beans beans
beans beans beans
beans beans beans
beans beans beans
beans beans beans

_____

_____

3.

mo**once**on

_____

_____

4.

once
9:45am

_____

_____

5.

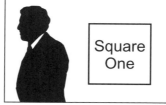

Square
One

_____

_____

6.

_____

_____

Test 22: Proofreading

You have **10 minutes** to do this test. Work as quickly and accurately as you can.

> Choose the right word or phrase to complete the gap.
> Circle the letter which matches the correct word.

1. The guests were welcome to come at any time **after between on until by**
                                                                  A   B   C   D   E

2. one and three o'clock. Emma **won't must should need did** have been
                           A   B   C   D   E

3. ready, **unless but that despite anyway** she couldn't find her dress. She
        A   B   C   D   E

4. realised that she had **wears worn weared wear wearing** it to Simon's
              A   B   C   D   E

party last week, so it must be somewhere in her wardrobe.

> This passage has some spelling mistakes.
> Write the passage out again with the correct spellings.

5. "You'll never beleive what I just saw!" Joe exclamed from the other end of the corridoor. He ran towards his group of friends but triped over his own feet.

_____

_____

_____

In each line there is one punctuation mistake. Circle the letter which matches the part of the sentence with the mistake.

6. Dan and Karen were due to be married in july, the hottest month of the year.

   A   B   C   D   E

7. I was shocked, to find out how expensive the cakes were at the café.

   A   B   C   D   E

8. "I'm afraid to say I've never met the man. Hes known to be quite mysterious."

   A   B   C   D   E

9. She drew one last, breath and dived underwater to tickle Mary's feet.

   A   B   C   D   E

10. While tuning his guitar the musician greeted a group of onlookers.

    A   B   C   D   E

11. The greengrocer had just restocked his supply of broccoli and courgette's.

    A   B   C   D   E

12. "How much does that come to then, young man," the lady asked the waiter.

    A   B   C   D   E

13. Eighty miles' south of the border was a little village famous for its cheese.

    A   B   C   D   E

END OF TEST

/ 16

You have **10 minutes** to do this test. Work as quickly and accurately as you can.

Read this passage carefully and answer the questions that follow.

Gold Rush

Splash. Splash. Shuffle. Shuffle. Splash. Carson stood up and arched his back. It felt good to stretch after hours hunched over his pan. A bead of sweat prickled his brow and he wiped it away with the back of his hand. Although the sun was dipping behind the mountains, it was still sweltering — at least his feet were submerged in
5 the shallows of the cool river. He looked down at his pan and sighed. Stones, silt, sand — every day was the same. Last week, he'd heard of a group of prospectors* up north who'd found a nugget as large as a plum. Of course, it could just be a tall tale, but the thought of finding his fortune lying on the river bed thrilled him to his core. His parents had never fully supported his decision to become a prospector,
10 and he was desperate to make them proud.

At last, the shadows were beginning to lengthen, and a papery moon hung in the sky. Some of his fellow prospectors waded out of the shallows, rolled down their trouser legs and stowed their pans in burlap sacks. It wouldn't be long before the air would be heavy with woodsmoke, charring meat and the low murmur of voices.
15 *Splash. Splash. Shuffle. Shuffle. Splash.* Carson wondered how much longer he should keep going in the dim light. His toes were wrinkled like prunes. *Splash. Splash. Shuffle. Shuffle. Splash.* Three more, he told himself. *Splash. Splash. Shuffle. Shuffle. Splash.* He was about to submerge his pan once more when he saw it. It wasn't as large as a plum, but it was unmistakably gold. He brought his
20 pan closer to his face, his breath caught in his throat.

"Whatcha got there, Carson?" called a gruff voice from up the river.

"N-n-nothing," stammered Carson, immediately pulling the pan away from his face. "False alarm. Just a piece of glass catchin' the sun," he said with a shrug. He waved at the man with the gruff voice and, as calmly as he could, waded out of the river.

prospectors — people who search for gold

1.   What is Carson doing in the river?

   _____

2.   Find a word from the text that means the same as "hot".

   _____

3.   "a nugget as large as a plum" (line 7). What is this phrase an example of?
     Tick the box next to the correct answer.

   A   Simile   ☐

   B   Metaphor   ☐

   C   Alliteration ☐

   D   Rhyme   ☐

4.   What does the phrase "tall tale" (line 8) mean?

   _____

5.   In your own words, explain how Carson's parents feel about him being a prospector.

   _____

   _____

TURN OVER ➡

6. Why do some of the prospectors leave the river?
Tick the box next to the correct answer.

    A   They're getting cold. ☐

    B   It's getting dark. ☐

    C   They're afraid their burlap sacks will get stolen. ☐

    D   They need to put out a fire. ☐

7. "immediately pulling the pan away from his face" (line 22). What type of word is "immediately"? Tick the box next to the correct answer.

    A   Verb ☐

    B   Adverb ☐

    C   Noun ☐

    D   Adjective ☐

8. Explain why Carson wades out of the river "calmly" (line 24).

_____

9. According to the passage, which of the following statements is false?
Tick the box next to the correct answer.

    A   Carson doesn't care what his family thinks. ☐

    B   The river is near mountains. ☐

    C   Carson has spent many hours in the river. ☐

    D   Carson is not the only person in the river. ☐

END OF TEST

/ 9

You have **10 minutes** to do this test. Work as quickly and accurately as you can.

> Choose the right word or phrase to complete the gap.
> Circle the letter which matches the correct word.

1. Marzia   **spending**   **spends**   **spents**   **spend**   **spent**   the afternoon
              A   **B**   **C**   **D**   **E**

2. daydreaming in her room. She should   **have**   **be**   **of**   **off**   **is**   been in school
                                         A   **B**   **C**   **D**   **E**

3. today, but the school was   **snowy**   **snown**   **snow**   **snows**   **snowed**   in,
                            A   **B**   **C**   **D**   **E**

4. meaning that lessons   **which**   **would**   **was**   **were**   **where**   cancelled all day.
                     A   **B**   **C**   **D**   **E**

> This passage has some punctuation mistakes.
> Write the passage out again with the correct punctuation.

5. All morning Richard had been baking a cake for his wife. He wasnt a very good
    baker, so he called her "down for help". She was furious that she had to help.

    _____

    _____

    _____

TURN OVER ➡

6. In early spring, the farmer rounds up his gotes so he can milk them.

    A   B   C   D   E

7. Building their nests high up provides birds with protecsion from predators.

    A   B   C   D   E

8. The pursonal trainer told the man to do fifty press-ups to improve his strength.

    A   B   C   D   E

9. Vicky carelessly splashed milk over her cerial as she was in a rush to get to work.

    A   B   C   D   E

10. He worked tyrelessly through the night on his project about volcanic eruptions.

    A   B   C   D   E

11. She selected the finest pare of woollen socks she had from her wardrobe.

    A   B   C   D   E

12. The scientist studied the fossils, carefully examening each one in turn.

    A   B   C   D   E

13. Liam missed his breaktime for a week because of his bad behavour.

    A   B   C   D   E

END OF TEST

/ 16

Time for a break! This puzzle is a great way to practise your **word-making** skills.

The Word Factory

The word factory takes nouns and turns them into verbs and adjectives.
A customer has a letter that needs verbs and adjectives. Put the words through
the verb and adjective machines and fill in the missing words in the letter below.
Each word should only be used once.

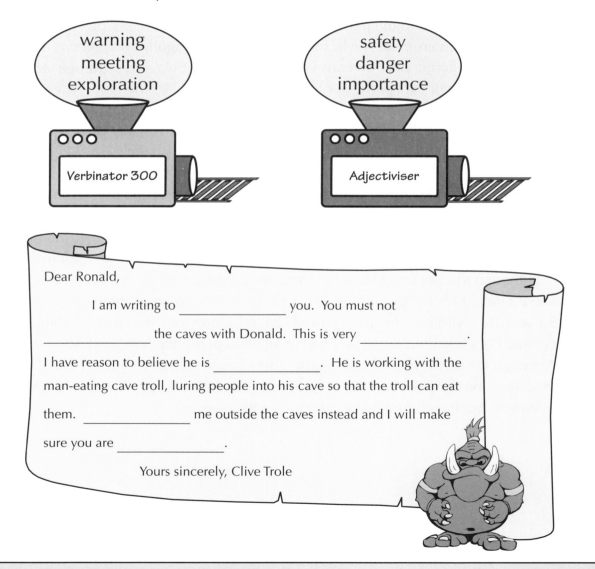

warning
meeting
exploration

Verbinator 300

safety
danger
importance

Adjectiviser

Dear Ronald,

I am writing to _____ you. You must not _____ the caves with Donald. This is very _____.

I have reason to believe he is _____. He is working with the man-eating cave troll, luring people into his cave so that the troll can eat them. _____ me outside the caves instead and I will make sure you are _____.

Yours sincerely, Clive Trole

Test 25: Comprehension

You have **10 minutes** to do this test. Work as quickly and accurately as you can.

> Read this passage carefully and answer the questions that follow.

Uncle Fat

Have you ever been at the British seaside and found yourself surrounded by greedy seagulls as soon as you start tucking into your fish and chips? What about having a nice picnic in the park only to be confronted by a pesky pigeon pecking at your sandwich crumbs? Well, some animals, like seagulls and pigeons, have
5 learned that loitering near humans is one of the easiest ways to scavenge for food, and this behaviour isn't particular to animals in the UK. In Thailand, macaques (a type of monkey) are very common and they often congregate near tourist attractions because they know that they can stuff themselves silly on scraps from visitors. Perhaps the most famous macaque in Thailand is Uncle Fat — a monkey
10 who has gorged himself on so much leftover junk food that he has an enormous pot belly and is now three times the size of an average macaque. His massive size means he's not as nimble as the other macaques, but this hasn't stopped him from getting the best scraps. Because he's the leader of a troop of monkeys, the other members of the troop scavenge for him and bring Uncle Fat the choicest leftovers.
15 Although tourists find Uncle Fat amusing, conservation groups became worried about Uncle Fat's health and the effect all the junk food was having on his body. So, in 2017, wildlife officials captured Uncle Fat and took him to a rehabilitation centre. He's been put on a strict diet in an attempt to help him shed some weight. Although Uncle Fat is an extreme case, there has been some concern that if
20 macaques become dependent on handouts from humans they'll not only become a nuisance, but they'll forget how to hunt for themselves.

Answer these questions about the text. You can refer back to the text if you need to.

1. Explain why the author describes the seagulls as "greedy" (line 2).

_____

_____

2. "pesky pigeon pecking" (line 3). What is this phrase an example of? Tick the box next to the correct answer.

    A   Metaphor   ☐

    B   Simile   ☐

    C   Alliteration   ☐

    D   Personification   ☐

3. "this behaviour isn't particular to animals in the UK" (line 6). Explain what this means in your own words.

_____

_____

4. Explain why macaques can be found near tourist attractions.

_____

5. Explain how Uncle Fat got the best food despite not being very mobile.

_____

_____

TURN OVER ➡

Test 25

6. Find a word from the text that means the same as "funny".

_____

7. Explain why Uncle Fat was taken to a rehabilitation centre.

_____

8. Which of the words below is closest in meaning to the word "extreme" (line 19)?
   Tick the box next to the correct answer.

   A   Exceptional   ☐

   B   Serious   ☐

   C   Ridiculous   ☐

   D   Famous   ☐

9. Which one of the following is given as a consequence of humans feeding macaques junk food? Tick the box next to the correct answer.

   A   Macaques will refuse to eat healthy food.   ☐

   B   Macaques will stop visiting tourist attractions.   ☐

   C   Lots of macaques will have to be put on a diet.   ☐

   D   Macaques will forget how to hunt.   ☐

END OF TEST

/ 9

You have **10 minutes** to do this test. Work as quickly and accurately as you can.

> This passage contains some spelling mistakes.
> Write the passage out again with the correct spellings.

1. The fotographer pointed her camera towards the celebrities walking down the red carpit. She presed the buton, hoping to get a good shot.

_____

_____

_____

> This passage has some punctuation mistakes.
> Write the passage out again with the correct punctuation.

2. Its believed that fireworks were invented in china in the seventh Century. However, fireworks wouldnt become popular in Europe for another thousand years.

_____

_____

_____

TURN OVER

3. The rangers waited quietly **off in since down through** the bushes. Some
A   B   C   D   E

4. of the locals had **tolded telling told telled tell** them that people had come to
A   B   C   D   E

5. hunt in the area. Rudi **taken tooked taked take took** a pair of binoculars
A   B   C   D   E

6. from his satchel and **brought bringed bring brung brang** them to his eyes.
A   B   C   D   E

7. "What **does are be have do** you see?" Piet asked through gritted
A   B   C   D   E

8. teeth. A group of lions were **lying lay lie lied lies** down, enjoying
A   B   C   D   E

9. **her this our his their** afternoon nap. A band of hunters lurked
A   B   C   D   E

10. **with front on after behind** some nearby bushes.
A   B   C   D   E

"Poachers," Rudi snarled in disgust.

END OF TEST

/ 16

You have **10 minutes** to do this test. Work as quickly and accurately as you can.

Read this poem carefully and answer the questions that follow.

The Peppery Man

The Peppery Man was cross and thin;
He scolded* out and scolded in;
He shook his fist, his hair he tore;
He stamped his feet and slammed the door.

5 Heigh ho, the Peppery Man,
The rabid*, crabbed* Peppery Man!
Oh, never since the world began
Was anyone like the Peppery Man.

His ugly temper was so sour
10 He often scolded for an hour;
He gnashed his teeth and stormed and scowled,
He snapped and snarled and yelled and howled.

He wore a fierce and savage frown;
He scolded up and scolded down;
15 He scolded over field and glen,
And then he scolded back again.

*scolded — *told off*
*rabid — *angry*
*crabbed — *cross*
*chafed — *was annoyed*
*vexed — *angry*

His neighbours, when they heard his roars,
Closed their blinds and locked their doors,
Shut their windows, sought their beds,
20 Stopped their ears and covered their heads.

He fretted, chafed*, and boiled and fumed;
With fiery rage he was consumed,
And no one knew, when he was vexed*,
What in the world would happen next.

25 Heigh ho, the Peppery Man,
The rabid, crabbed Peppery Man!
Oh, never since the world began
Was anyone like the Peppery Man.

Arthur Macy

TURN OVER ➡

Answer these questions about the text. You can refer back to the text if you need to.

1. Which of the following words best describes what the Peppery Man looks like? Tick the box next to the correct answer.

   A   Bald   ☐

   B   Ugly   ☐

   C   Tall   ☐

   D   Slim   ☐

2. Which of the following isn't given as a sign that the Peppery Man is angry? Tick the box next to the correct answer.

   A   He shakes his fist.   ☐

   B   He complains to his neighbours. ☐

   C   He slams doors.   ☐

   D   He tears his hair out.   ☐

3. Find and copy a word from the text that means the same as "shouted".

   _____

4. "He wore a fierce and savage frown" (line 13). Which of these words is a noun? Tick the box next to the correct answer.

   A   wore   ☐

   B   a   ☐

   C   savage ☐

   D   frown   ☐

5. "He scolded **over** field and glen" (line 15). What is the word in bold an example of?

_____

6. How do the Peppery Man's neighbours know when he is angry?

_____

7. Explain in your own words how the Peppery Man's neighbours react when he is angry.

_____

_____

8. "With fiery rage he was consumed" (line 22). Explain what this line means in your own words.

_____

9. Which of the words below best describes the Peppery Man when he is angry? Tick the box next to the correct answer.

A   Quiet   ☐

B   Unpredictable   ☐

C   Reasonable   ☐

D   Short-lived   ☐

END OF TEST

/ 9

It's now time to practise your knowledge of **homophones**.

Homnomnoms

Victor's pies are so popular that he has to write his recipes in a secret code to stop rival bakers from stealing them. He has written a clue to remind him of a word that sounds the same as the ingredient. Below, write the homophone based on the clue and then the ingredient he needs to use.

Savoury pie		Homophone		Ingredient
water escaped from a pipe	➡	l _ _ _	➡	_ _ _ _
a post driven into the ground	➡	s _ _ _ _ _	➡	_ _ _ _ _
has visited somewhere	➡	b _ _ _	➡	_ _ _ _

Sweet pie				
hide something underground	➡	b _ _ _ _	➡	_ _ _ _ _ _
a set of two things	➡	p _ _ _	➡	_ _ _ _
the pretty part of a plant	➡	f _ _ _ _ _	➡	_ _ _ _ _

You have **10 minutes** to do this test. Work as quickly and accurately as you can.

> Choose the right word or phrase to complete the gap.
> Circle the letter which matches the correct word.

1. Nigel **would should couldn't ought won't** wait to go to the cinema tonight.
        A   B   C   D   E

2. He was sitting **on in at through over** his classroom waiting for the
        A B C   D   E

3. bell to ring. When it eventually chimed, he **running runned ran run runs**
        A   B   C D E

4. outside and was home **over outside at within before** five minutes.
        A   B   C   D   E

> This passage has some spelling mistakes.
> Write the passage out again with the correct spellings.

5. The wether had been beatiful all day, and Sophia had been relaxing on the beach.
    She went for a swim in the see, but it was freezing cold. She couldn't stop shivvering.

_____

_____

_____

TURN OVER ➡

6. Lucys parents had been dragging her round the shops all day and she was bored.

| A | B | C | D | E |

7. Lewis had bought a new pair of trainers and he was worried they wouldnt fit.

| A | B | C | D | E |

8. I'm making a carrot cake recipe that contains flour eggs, carrots, sugar and butter.

| A | B | C | D | E |

9. I heard someone shouting my name. "Nick! How's it going? Karen said.

| A | B | C | D | E |

10. "What are you doing tonight," asked Rachel. "Do you want to go to the park?"

| A | B | C | D | E |

11. Aaron was panicking about his exam on Thursday He'd not done any revision.

| A | B | C | D | E |

12. More people live in Moscow, the capital, of Russia, than in London.

| A | B | C | D | E |

13. We have a new dog whos very nervous and refuses to sleep in his basket.

| A | B | C | D | E |

END OF TEST

/ 16

You have **10 minutes** to do this test. Work as quickly and accurately as you can.

> Choose the right word or phrase to complete the gap.
> Circle the letter which matches the correct word.

1. Craig was looking **at** **in** **towards** **forward** **for** to eating his lunch.
                   A **B**   **C**   **D**   **E**

2. He **has** **were** **had** **was** **will** made an enormous tuna sandwich.
        A   **B**   **C**   **D**   **E**

3. When he **going** **come** **comes** **went** **go** to the fridge to get it, it had gone!
           A   **B**   **C**   **D** **E**

4. A trail of crumbs **lead** **following** **leaded** **led** **follows** Craig to the culprit.
              A   **B**   **C**   **D**   **E**

> This passage has some punctuation mistakes.
> Write the passage out again with the correct punctuation.

5. "Aah! Shrieked Harry as a mouse ran across the kitchen. He jumped on a chair and refused to come down The mouse saw he was scared and went about his business' as slowly as possible.

_____

_____

_____

TURN OVER ➡

          81   Test 29

6. We took the rickety old ferry to the little iland in the middle of the lake.

A	B	C	D	E

7. "Do you know Rani's adress? I have no idea which street she lives on."

A	B	C	D	E

8. I baked twelve biscuits and left them on the counter. Six have dissapeared.

A	B	C	D	E

9. Frank was not intrested in football, but he still played every day at lunchtime.

A	B	C	D	E

10. Barbara's freshly baked scones where selling quickly. Business was booming!

A	B	C	D	E

11. Yesterday, Nicola brout sweets in for her whole class because it was her birthday.

A	B	C	D	E

12. London is the second most poplar city to visit in the world, after Bangkok.

A	B	C	D	E

13. Spending too long in the bath can make your fingers all rinkly.

A	B	C	D	E

END OF TEST

/ 16

You have **10 minutes** to do this test. Work as quickly and accurately as you can.

Read this passage carefully and answer the questions that follow.

The Everglades

Sometimes referred to as the "River of Grass", the Everglades is an enormous region of tropical wetlands in Florida in the southern United States. It is home to many species not found elsewhere in the US. The Everglades was made a national park in 1947 and is the third biggest national park in the US (not including national
5   parks in Alaska). It is often thought to be a large swamp or marsh, but in actual fact it's a very large and slow-moving river, that flows from just south of Orlando, into the sea.

A wide variety of plants and animals live in the Everglades, and its tropical climate means that its wildlife is very different from elsewhere in North America.
10 Perhaps its most famous residents are alligators, who prowl the waterways of Florida. Crocodiles also live in Florida, mostly in saltwater, coastal areas. Crocodiles can be told apart from alligators by their V-shaped snout, which differs from the alligator's more rounded nose. Alligators might be fearsome predators, but there's no need to worry. Most alligators are too small to really hurt humans, and attacks are rare —
15 more people in the US are killed by cows than by alligators and crocodiles.

Another, gentler animal that calls the Everglades home is the manatee. These large, slow-moving mammals swim in coastal waters, grazing on seagrass and leaves. They spend over half their day eating and are often referred to as 'sea cows'.

The most endangered animal to live in the Everglades is the Florida panther, a
20 large cat that lives in the forests around the wetlands. It is estimated that there are only around 160 left in the wild.

TURN OVER ➡

Answer these questions about the text. You can refer back to the text if you need to.

1. Why do you think the Everglades is called the "River of Grass" (line 1)?

_____

_____

2. Why do you think the Everglades is home to species not found elsewhere in North America? Tick the box next to the correct answer.

    A   The Everglades is a national park. ☐

    B   It has a tropical climate, unlike most of North America. ☐

    C   There are too many people in other parts of North America. ☐

    D   The Everglades is far away from other parts of the US. ☐

3. Find and copy a word or phrase from the text that means the same as the verb "stalk".

_____

4. According to the text, how can you tell crocodiles and alligators apart? Tick the box next to the correct answer.

    A   Alligators prey on people and crocodiles do not. ☐

    B   Only alligators live in Florida. ☐

    C   They have different shaped snouts. ☐

    D   Crocodiles are much smaller than alligators. ☐

5. "fearsome" (line 13) as it is used in the text is an example of which type of word?

_____

6. Which of these animals kills the most people in the US?
Tick the box next to the correct answer.

A   Alligator   ☐

B   Manatee   ☐

C   Cows   ☐

D   Crocodile   ☐

7. Why do you think that manatees are referred to as "sea cows" (line 18)?

_____

8. What does the word "estimated" (line 20) mean as it is used in the text?
Tick the box next to the correct answer.

A   Known   ☐

B   Counted   ☐

C   Included   ☐

D   Guessed   ☐

9. Give the name of an animal mentioned in the text that lives in the Everglades but not in the water.

_____

END OF TEST

/ 9

Phew... Almost done. These puzzles will help you practise your **spelling** and **logic** skills.

Treasure Hunt Tricks

Some treasure has been buried at one of the locations marked with a letter below. Five people have given clues — but beware! Anyone who has made a spelling mistake is lying! Circle the incorrect spellings and write the correct spelling on the lines, then use the clues to find the location of the treasure.

Claude says: The treasure is behind the restaraunt. _____

Jill says: The statue isn't on the left of the treasure. _____

Philippa says: The cathedrel is nowhere near the treasure. _____

Karl says: To the rite of the treasure is the forest. _____

Urslan says: It's betwen the skyscraper and the forest. _____

You have **10 minutes** to do this test. Work as quickly and accurately as you can.

This passage contains some spelling mistakes.
Write the passage out again with the correct spellings.

1. Martin had spent all night on his histery homework. He was doing a project on the Tudors, but he found doing his own reserch quite dificult. His dad had been too bisy to give him any help.

_____

_____

_____

_____

This passage has some punctuation mistakes.
Write the passage out again with the correct punctuation.

2. Wendys sister is having a birthday party on saturday. although Wendy had tried to bake her a cake she had burnt it and had to buy one instead.

_____

_____

_____

TURN OVER ➡

Test 31

Choose the right word or phrase to complete the gap.
Circle the letter which matches the correct word.

3. James's mum **dropped** **drops** **drop** **dropping** **drips** James and Joe off at the
                A   **B**   **C**   **D**   **E**

4. airport. Then, suddenly, Joe looked panicked. **Putted** **Pat** **Patted** **Putted** **Patting**
                                             A   **B**   **C**   **D**   **E**

5. down his pockets, he exclaimed, "I've **forgetting** **forgotten** **forgot** **forget** **forgetted**
                                       A   **B**   **C**   **D**   **E**

6. my passport! And the plane **went** **left** **sets** **come** **leaves** in half an hour!"
                      A   **B**   **C**   **D**   **E**

7. They **begin** **beginned** **began** **begun** **begins** to run after James's mum's car,
       A   **B**   **C**   **D**   **E**

8. which they could still **watched** **saw** **see** **look** **watch** in the distance.
                     A   **B**   **C**   **D**   **E**

9. They were **shout** **screamed** **shouted** **shouts** **shouting** frantically when James
             A   **B**   **C**   **D**   **E**

10. realised he'd just **pack** **put** **putted** **packing** **puts** his passport in his bag!
                    A   **B**   **C**   **D**   **E**

END OF TEST

/ 16

Test 32: Comprehension

You have **10 minutes** to do this test. Work as quickly and accurately as you can.

Read this passage carefully and answer the questions that follow.

Alien Encounter

Will was woken by a loud bang. Storms had been forecast for that evening, so he assumed it was just a crack of thunder. He slowly rubbed his eyes and looked at his watch — 3 am. He rolled over and tried to get back to sleep, but a bright white glow was shining through his curtains. Furiously, he pulled the curtains wide open and

5 saw that the strange glow was coming from the bottom of his garden. His irritation suddenly turned to curiosity.

He tiptoed cautiously down the stairs, trying not to wake his parents. He opened the back door and ventured outside. From here, he got a better view of what was causing the strange, luminous glow. A miniature spaceship, shaped like a frisbee,

10 was lying on the flower beds under the tree. Tiny, human-like creatures, glowing in the darkness, scuttled hectically around the spacecraft, quickly chattering in a squeaky, alien language.

Will was not easily frightened, so he continued walking slowly towards the glow, fascinated by his strange visitors. He moved as quietly as a mouse, not wanting to

15 spook the mysterious creatures. The light from the object was blinding him and he struggled to see where he was going, but he carried on. Suddenly, he felt a thump — he'd walked into a tree and hit his head.

Hours later, he was woken up by his mother. It was daylight and the strange object had vanished. His mum looked worried and kept asking why he was lying in her

20 flower beds. He didn't tell her the truth. There's no way she would have believed it.

TURN OVER ➡️

Answer these questions about the text. You can refer back to the text if you need to.

1. What does Will think caused the loud bang?
   Tick the box next to the correct answer.

   A   A spaceship   ☐

   B   A dog   ☐

   C   His window opening   ☐

   D   Thunder   ☐

2. Which word below best describes how Will is feeling when he goes to open his curtains?

   A   Annoyed   ☐

   B   Eager   ☐

   C   Terrified   ☐

   D   Bewildered   ☐

3. Give another word that means the same as "hectically" (line 11) as it is used in the text.

   _____

4. "quickly chattering in a squeaky alien language" (lines 11-12).
   Which of these words is an adverb?

   _____

5. Describe in your own words how Will is feeling as he approaches the spaceship.

   _____

   _____

6. What is "as quietly as a mouse" (line 14) an example of?
Tick the box next to the correct answer.

   A   Metaphor   ☐

   B   Alliteration   ☐

   C   Simile   ☐

   D   Personification   ☐

7. Why does Will walk towards the spaceship quietly?
Tick the box next to the correct answer.

   A   He didn't want to wake his parents.   ☐

   B   He didn't want to scare the creatures.   ☐

   C   He didn't want to trip up in the dark.   ☐

   D   He was too sleepy to go quickly.   ☐

8. Why is Will asleep in the garden? Tick the box next to the correct answer.

   A   He was really sleepy.   ☐

   B   The creatures hit him on the head.   ☐

   C   He walked into a tree and passed out.   ☐

   D   He tripped over and passed out.   ☐

9. Why doesn't Will tell his mother about the spaceship?

   _____

END OF TEST

/ 9

91

You have **10 minutes** to do this test. Work as quickly and accurately as you can.

Read this passage carefully and answer the questions that follow.

The Green Children of Woolpit

During the Middle Ages, in the otherwise ordinary village of Woolpit in rural Suffolk, a strange event took place — at least if you believe the legends.

The villagers had a shock one day when, coming back from the harvest, they discovered two children with bright green skin. The brother and sister spoke an
5   unknown language and wore strange clothes. Despite being noticeably starved, they bizarrely refused to eat anything other than raw broad beans. Eventually, they began to eat a normal diet, learnt to speak English and lost their green hue. The boy fell sick and died, but the girl told the villagers that she came from a mysterious place called St. Martin's Land, where people lived underground and everyone was
10   green. According to the girl, the sun never shone in St. Martin's Land. She said that they had been looking after their father's cattle when they followed the animals into a cave. They then followed the sound of bells and came out on the other side at Woolpit into bright sunlight, which they found startling.

There are many theories as to who the green children of Woolpit really were.
15   Many say it is simply a local folk legend made up by the villagers. Others even believe that the children were aliens! Some have given a more rational explanation of the events. One idea is that they were orphans from Belgium whose parents were killed in Suffolk. According to this theory, the language they were speaking was Flemish (a Belgian language) and their green skin was due to a very poor diet.
20   Today, the story of the green children of Woolpit is a mystery which continues to fascinate new generations.

Answer these questions about the text. You can refer back to the text if you need to.

1.   Give one thing that was strange about the children's appearance.

_____

2. What kind of word is "unknown" (line 5)?

_____

3. Which of the words below is closest in meaning to the word "noticeably" (line 5)?
Tick the box next to the correct answer.

   A   Clearly ☐

   B   Noticed ☐

   C   Uncertainly ☐

   D   Secretly ☐

4. Why was it "bizarre" that they refused to eat anything other than broad beans?

_____

5. According to the girl's story, how did the children get to Woolpit?
Tick the box next to the correct answer.

   A   On a boat ☐

   B   On a spaceship ☐

   C   They went into a cave and came out in Woolpit. ☐

   D   They tripped and fell down a hole. ☐

TURN OVER ➡

6. Why did the children find the sunlight "startling" (line 13)?

_____

_____

7. Which of these is not given as a theory about the origins of the story?
   Tick the box next to the correct answer.

   A   It was made up by the villagers. ☐

   B   The children were orphans from Belgium. ☐

   C   The children were aliens. ☐

   D   The children were playing a prank. ☐

8. According to the "rational explanation" (line 16), why were the children green?
   Tick the box next to the correct answer.

   A   They were from St. Martin's Land. ☐

   B   They were ill. ☐

   C   They had a poor diet. ☐

   D   They had eaten too many broad beans. ☐

9. Give another word that means the same as "fascinate" (line 21)
   as it is used in the text.

   _____

END OF TEST

/ 9

E4XPE1

CGP

11+
English

Ages
8-9

The
Answer Book

English

Practise • Prepare • Pass
Everything your child needs for 11+ success

E4XPE1

Test 1 — pages 2-4

1. B
Line 3 states that Anya gets "worked up" over Jordan's scary stories, meaning she is upset by them. This suggests that thinking about them is the reason she cannot sleep.

2. various answers possible
E.g. "left no stone unturned" means 'searched everywhere'.

3. A
Line 11 states that Harvey was "a hurricane of energy". Therefore, he can be described as energetic.

4. B
'abnormal' and 'unusual' both mean 'out of the ordinary'.

5. under
'under' is a preposition because it describes the location of something.

6. She feels frightened when she hears the noise.
Lines 17-18 state that after hearing the noise, Anya "sat bolt upright in bed and froze". This suggests that the noise frightened her.

7. various answers possible
E.g. 'dragging' means the same as 'pulling' or 'heaving'.

8. She feels relieved that it wasn't a monster making the noise.
Line 26 states that "Anya let out a huge sigh and fell back on her bed" after seeing Harvey. That she is able to relax on the bed suggests it was a sigh of relief after she realises that it was just Harvey making the noise.

9. C
Line 3 states that Jordan "knew how worked up" Anya got over his stories. This suggests that Jordan does realise how scary Anya finds his stories.

Test 2 — pages 5-6

1. Spring is my favo<u>u</u>rite time of year. The bare trees and he<u>d</u>ges become green and lush; birdsong can be heard in the treetops; and lambs skip in the fi<u>el</u>ds. Sudd<u>en</u>ly, the landscape is alive after a long and sleepy winter.
The bits that are underlined show where a spelling mistake has been corrected. You get one mark for each of the following words you have spelt correctly: 'favourite', 'hedges', 'fields' and 'Suddenly'.

2. I grabbed some biscuits from the shelf<u>.</u> <u>"</u>Put those back<u>!"</u> said Mum.
The bits that are underlined show where punctuation has been corrected. You get one mark for each of the following: a full stop after 'shelf'; speech marks before 'Put'; an exclamation mark (or comma) after 'back'; and speech marks after the exclamation mark (or comma).

3. A
'made' is correct because it is the correct past tense form of the verb 'to make'.

4. C
'were' is correct because it's in the past tense and agrees with the pronoun 'we'.

5. B
'couldn't' is correct because it makes the most sense in this sentence.

6. C
'found' is correct because it's the correct past tense form of the verb 'to find'.

7. D
'sat' is correct because it's the correct past tense form of the verb 'to sit'.

8. D
'love' is correct because it agrees with the pronoun 'I'.

9. B
'is' is correct because it makes the most sense in this sentence.

10. B
'decided' is correct because it's the correct past tense form of the verb 'to decide'.

Test 3 — pages 7-9

1. various answers possible
E.g. a distant place. 'far-flung' means 'distant' or 'remote' and 'location' means 'place'.

2. C
'magnificent mountains' is an example of alliteration because both words begin with the same letter.

3. A
To 'cast a spell' over someone means 'to charm' or 'to enchant' them. This means the same as 'to fascinate' them.

4. various answers possible
E.g. The Cuillins are "the most challenging peaks in Britain" (line 4) which means they are the perfect place for climbers to go to test their skills.

5. craggy
"craggy" (line 5) means the same as 'rocky'.

6. A
'incredibly' is an adverb because it describes the adjective 'tough'.

7. C
Line 11 states that the Old Man of Storr "is a tall needle of rock".

8. It looks like somewhere fairies might live.
Line 17 states that the Fairy Glen "looks so enchanting you could almost believe that fairies really do live there". This suggests that it looks like somewhere fairies might live.

9. A

'encounter' and 'meet' both mean 'happen to see'.

Puzzles 1 — page 10

Dan's Den
various answers possible

E.g. Take the **narrow** path through the woods. Go right at the first **straight** tree. Cross the **shallowest** part of the stream over the stepping stones. The den is straight ahead, to the left of a **flimsy** gate. Knock **slowly** on the door five times.

Synonym Scramble

1. rush   hurry
2. heavy   weighty
3. smart   clever
4. support help
5. certain positive

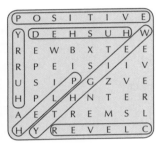

Test 4 — pages 11-12

1. E

'thought' is correct because it is the correct past tense form of the verb 'to think' which agrees with the tense of the rest of the passage.

2. B

'caught' is correct because it is the correct past tense form of the verb 'to catch' which agrees with the tense of the rest of the passage.

3. E

'though' is correct because it completes the phrase 'as though he hadn't'.

4. C

'might' makes the most sense in this sentence.

5.   That evening, my dad went to feed our cows and I jo<u>i</u>ned him. It always sc<u>a</u>res me the way they come h<u>u</u>rtling towards us, but Dad's calmness always reas<u>s</u>ures me.

The bits that are underlined show where a spelling mistake has been corrected. You get one mark for each of the following words you have spelt correctly: 'joined', 'scares', 'hurtling' and 'reassures'.

6. B

'Lauras' should be 'Laura's' — Laura is a singular noun, so the apostrophe should go before the 's'.

7. E

There should be a full stop after 'them' to mark the end of the sentence.

8. C

There should be speech marks after the comma after 'directions' because this is the end of speech.

9. C

'Tomorrow' should be 'tomorrow' — 'tomorrow' is not a proper noun, so it doesn't need a capital letter.

10. D

There should be a comma between 'pool' and 'sauna' to separate the items in the list.

11. D

There should be a question mark after 'weekend' instead of a comma because Debs is asking a question.

12. B

'mums' should be 'mum's' — an apostrophe is needed here because the best friend belongs to mum.

13. A

There shouldn't be a comma after 'Karina'.

Test 5 — pages 13-15

1.   various answers possible

E.g. 'crunch' means the same as 'chomp', 'gnaw' or 'chew'.

2.   C

Line 11 states that "oysters can slumber in pails". 'Slumber' means 'sleep' and 'pail' means 'bucket', so the oysters sleep in buckets.

3.   Lambs live in fenced off areas where they are protected from bad weather.

'enclosed' means 'surrounded on all sides' and 'exposed' means 'left unprotected', so this line means that the lambs are protected from bad weather in a fenced or walled off place.

4.   A

"stable" is mentioned in line 10, "Coops" are mentioned in line 16 and "pens" are mentioned in line 18.

5.   D

Lines 22-23 state that "People would laugh if you rode a giraffe, / Or mounted the back of an ox". Therefore, the poem suggests that people would find it funny if they saw someone riding an ox.

6.   A

This is a simile because the snake is being compared to a hole in the ground by using the word 'as'.

7.   sleek

"sleek" (line 30) means the same as 'glossy'.

8.   straighter

'straighter' is the adjective because it describes the noun 'alligator'.

9. C

At the end of every verse, the camel has a different complaint about how he isn't treated as well as other animals. E.g. In the first verse, he talks about the different foods that other animals are given to eat, but says that "there's never a question / About MY digestion — / Anything does for me!" He is complaining that, in contrast to other animals, no-one cares what he is fed.

Test 6 — pages 16-18

1. unnoticed

'overlooked' and "unnoticed" (line 1) both mean 'not recognised'.

2. various answers possible

'iron' is a strong metal, so calling him 'Iron Joss' implies that he's strong. He has shown his strength through the various records he has set.

3. A

'superhuman' and 'incredible' both mean 'extraordinary'.

4. B

'determined' means 'not letting anything stop you'. Joss shows determination by not letting his back problems stop him from being active.

5. noun

'race' and 'sheep' are both things.

6. C

'he' refers to 'Joss Naylor', so it is a pronoun.

7. various answers possible

E.g. Line 13 states that "All his time spent herding sheep on the fells" had prepared him because he was fit and knew the fells well.

8. C

Lines 11-12 state that "by the age of 24, he ... took up running" so Joss didn't give up running when he was 24.

9. various answers possible

E.g. Joss is famous in the Lake District, but he is not well known elsewhere.

Puzzles 2 — page 19

Coming to Life

E.g. The leaf danced in the wind.
E.g. The ice skater was a graceful swan.
E.g. The wolf had teeth like knives.
E.g. She sang like a bird.
E.g. The cyclist was as fast as a rocket.

Test 7 — pages 20-21

1. D

'will' is correct because the sentence is about an event in the future.

2. A

'are' is correct because it completes the phrase 'There are only a few'.

3. C

'get' is correct because it is in the correct tense and agrees with the pronoun 'you'.

4. C

'avoid' is correct because it completes the phrase 'to avoid disappointment'.

5. Last week, I went to an art exhibition with my parents. After we had walked around and seen everything, we went for a meal at a restaurant.

The bits that are underlined show where punctuation has been corrected. You get one mark for each of the following: a comma after 'Last week'; a full stop after 'parents'; a comma after 'everything'; and a lower case 'r' in 'restaurant'.

6. E

'distanse' should be 'distance'.

7. B

'climed' should be 'climbed'.

8. D

'frends' should be 'friends'.

9. B

'towords' should be 'towards'.

10. D

'ornerment' should be 'ornament'.

11. C

'cleening' should be 'cleaning'.

12. C

'poynty' should be 'pointy'.

13. C

'befor' should be 'before'.

Test 8 — pages 22-24

1. C

'plump' and 'fat' both mean 'chunky'.

2. A

The snow is not actually a carpet — the author is comparing the snow to a carpet to suggest that the snow is covering everywhere — so this must be a metaphor.

3. B

Line 3 states that Lucy yells "excitedly". This suggests that she is happy about the snow, which means she feels delighted.

4. various answers possible

E.g. Line 9 states that Lucy grabs her dad's arm "imploringly" before asking "can we go sledging?". 'To implore' means 'to beg' which suggests that she grabs his arm to try and beg him to take her sledging.

5. various answers possible

E.g. Lucy feels disappointed when she first sees the slope. In line 17, Lucy says "This is it?" when she sees the "slight incline" in front of her. This suggests that she was expecting it to be higher and is disappointed by how small the hill actually is.

6.   C
'back in the day' means 'when I was younger'. Therefore, Lucy's dad is talking about sometime in the past.

7.   convinced
'persuaded' and 'convinced' (line 20) both mean 'certain about something'.

8.   because she is moving so slowly
Lines 23-24 state that Lucy's sledge "crawled along", meaning it moved very slowly. Lucy's dad is laughing because he had previously said that he had "picked up some serious speed on here back in the day" (lines 18-19) and it is funny that this has turned out to be untrue.

9.   D
Line 17 states that the hill had a "slight incline". 'slight' means 'small', and 'incline' means 'slope', therefore the hill wasn't very steep.

Test 9 — pages 25-26

1.   I went to the ki<u>tch</u>en to make a cup of tea. To my su<u>r</u>prise, there was a bird flying aro<u>und</u> in there. It must have flown in thr<u>ough</u> the window.
The bits that are underlined show where a spelling mistake has been corrected. You get one mark for each of the following words you have spelt correctly: 'kitchen', 'surprise', 'around' and 'through'.

2.   My mum has always wanted to go to Egypt, so we are taking her_as a present for her <u>b</u>irthday. She<u>'</u>s going to love it!
The bits that are underlined show where punctuation has been corrected. You get one mark for each of the following: a capital letter at the start of 'Egypt'; no full stop between 'her' and 'as'; no capital letter at the start of 'birthday'; and an apostrophe in 'She's'.

3.   B
'was' is correct because it is in the correct past tense form which agrees with the tense of the rest of the passage, and it agrees with 'Simon'.

4.   E
'longed' is correct because the passage is in the past tense.

5.   B
'with' is correct because it introduces what he was using to pluck his guitar strings.

6.   A
'he' is correct because it is referring back to Simon.

7.   D
'lots' is correct because it is the only option that can be followed by 'of'.

8.   E
'their' is correct because it shows that the winces belong to the tutors.

9.   C
'did' is correct because the passage is in the past tense.

10.   C
'easier' is correct because it completes the phrase 'something easier to play'.

Puzzles 3 — page 27

Letter Ladders

BARK	CRACK
BARE	TRACK
CARE	TRACE
CAPE	BRACE
COPE	BRAKE
CODE	BROKE
MODE	BLOKE

Hidden word: **clamber**

Test 10 — pages 28-29

1.   B
'any' is correct because it completes the phrase 'for any sign of'.

2.   C
'had' is correct because the passage is in the past tense and it completes the phrase 'He had been waiting'.

3.   E
'this' is the only word that makes sense in this sentence.

4.   E
'was' is correct because the passage is in the past tense and it makes the most sense in the sentence.

5.   The trees gro<u>a</u>ned and creaked as their bran<u>c</u>hes swayed in the howling wind. Bats flew he<u>re</u> and there and somewhere, an owl lo<u>u</u>dly hooted.
The bits that are underlined show where a spelling mistake has been corrected. You get one mark for each of the following words you have spelt correctly: 'groaned', 'branches', 'here', 'loudly'.

6.   D
There should be a comma after 'Iceland' to separate the countries in the list.

7.   A
There should be speech marks in front of 'Let's' to show that someone has started to speak.

8.   E
The exclamation mark should be a question mark because Josh is asking a question.

9.   A
'could'nt' should be 'couldn't'. This is a shortened version of 'could not', and the apostrophe replaces the missing letter 'o'.

10.   D
There should not be a comma after 'sky'.

11.   A
There should be a capital letter at the start of 'susie' because it is a person's name.

12. E
The speech marks after 'mum' aren't needed.

13. C
There should be an apostrophe in 'dog's', to show that the bowl belongs to the dog.

Test 11 — pages 30-32

1. They were chatting while walking.
Line 1 states that "Two friends once were walking in sociable chat". This means that they were chatting while they were walking.

2. C
'spied' and 'spotted' both mean 'saw'.

3. D
When the traveller finds the purse, he thanks his "fortune for that" (line 3) which suggests that he is thankful.

4. large
'large' is an adjective because it describes the noun 'sum'.

5. various answers possible
E.g. because he was there when his friend found the purse.

6. C
The traveller who found the purse states "He who found it the owner should be" (line 8). This means that he doesn't want to share the money with his friend which suggests that he is selfish.

7. The friend is accused of being a thief and a policeman comes.
In line 10, someone calls "Stop thief!" after them. This shows that the traveller who found the purse is accused of being a thief. Line 11 states that this person "comes with a policeman close in the rear!" This shows that a policeman is coming towards them.

8. B
'claimed' and 'taken' are verbs. They are both doing words.

9. A
Lines 15-16 state "since all the money was taken by you, / With you the problem lies". This suggests that the friend who didn't find the money will not help the other friend because he didn't share his money with him. Therefore, the moral of the poem is that if you share good things with your friends then they will help you in bad times.

Test 12 — pages 33-34

1. C
'along' is correct because it is the only word that makes sense in this sentence.

2. D
'in' is correct because it completes the phrase 'in the distance'.

3. E
'best' is correct because it is the only word that makes sense in this sentence.

4. B
'lots' is correct because it completes the phrase 'had lots of'.

5. I think it'd be really great to have a pet dragon. They can fly, breathe fire and they're really fierce. No-one would bother you if you had a pet dragon.
The bits that are underlined show where punctuation has been corrected. You get one mark for each of the following: an apostrophe in 'it'd'; a comma after 'fly'; an apostrophe in 'they're'; and no comma after 'you'.

6. E
'breth' should be 'breath'.

7. C
'munths' should be 'months'.

8. C
'rode' should be 'road'. These are homophones — 'road' is correct because it means 'a stretch of ground for cars to drive on' and 'rode' means 'to have been carried along on something'.

9. A
'visitted' should be 'visited' — there is no need to double the 't'.

10. E
'evrything' should be 'everything'.

11. D
'cofee' should be 'coffee' — the word is spelt with a double 'f'.

12. B
'berthday' should be 'birthday' — the root word is 'birth'.

13. E
'shaw' should be 'shore'.

Puzzles 4 — page 35

Cross Word

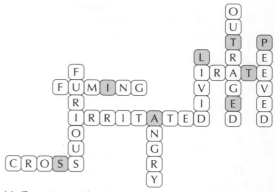

Mr. Ross is cross because he spilt tea.

Verb Picking
The verbs are: write, amuse, follow, grab, invent, hope.
The verb made from the letters in bold is **remove**.

Test 13 — pages 36-38

1.   D
In line 2, the narrator states "This was dull". 'Dull' means 'boring', which suggests that the narrator was bored.

2.   B
'heavily' and 'definitely' are adverbs.

3.   on the beach
In lines 3-5, the narrator states they would like to be "lying somewhere sandy, soaking up the sun and listening to the calming sound of the waves". This suggests that the narrator would rather be on the beach.

4.   C
'impressive' and 'remarkable' both mean 'extraordinary'.

5.   various answers possible
E.g. 'type' means the same as 'sort' or 'kind'.

6.   various answers possible
E.g. Lines 10-11 state that the narrator's parents were "fussing over different flowers and eagerly pointing things out to each other". This suggests that the narrator's parents are interested in the gardens and enjoy being there.

7.   the gift shop
Line 13 states that the narrator found the gift shop "the only tolerable part of the entire experience". This suggests that this was the part of visiting the garden that the narrator actually enjoyed.

8.   B
Line 15 states that the narrator's mum was "barely visible behind a pile of red leaves". This suggests that the plant was big enough to cover a person and had lots of leaves.

9.   various answers possible
E.g. The narrator feels annoyed because their mum is teasing them. In lines 21-22, she gave the narrator a "playful nudge" and the narrator "scowled".

Test 14 — pages 39-40

1.   My grandfather has won first prize for his gard<u>en</u> in the local compe<u>ti</u>tion. He came second last year, so he is real<u>ly</u> pleased. We are going with him on <u>S</u>aturday to collect his winnings.
The bits that are underlined show where a spelling mistake has been corrected. You get one mark for each of the following words you have spelt correctly: 'garden', 'competition', 'really' and 'Saturday'.

2.   Lucy<u>'</u>s cat, <u>B</u>ilbo, has got himself stuck up a tree again. Her mum<u>,</u> dad and brother are all outside trying to coax it down, but it isn<u>'</u>t working.
The bits that are underlined show where punctuation has been corrected. You get one mark for each of the following: an apostrophe in 'Lucy's'; a capital letter at the start of 'Bilbo'; a comma after 'mum'; and an apostrophe in 'isn't'.

3.   C
'often' is correct because it's the only option that can follow 'quite'.

4.   B
'slowly' is correct because it's an adverb that describes the verb 'drives'.

5.   A
'behind' makes the most sense in this sentence.

6.   E
'doing' is correct because it completes the phrase 'when it comes to doing'.

7.   B
'in' is correct because it completes the phrase 'taste in music'.

8.   D
'arriving' is correct because a verb following the phrase 'I enjoy' must end in 'ing'.

9.   D
'nodding' is correct because it is the only verb which agrees with the rest of the sentence.

10. A
'funny' is correct because it is an adjective which describes the friends' faces — the other words are verbs or nouns.

Test 15 — pages 41-43

1.   C
'harsh' is the adjective because it describes the noun 'climate'.

2.   It is too cold for humans to live there.
Lines 3-5 state that temperatures "fall to as low as -40°C, meaning it is almost impossible for humans" to live there.

3.   B
Line 12 states that polar bears are "extraordinarily strong". 'Strong' means the same as 'powerful', so polar bears can be described as powerful.

4.   Polar bears are described as 'fearsome predators' because of their strength and sharp teeth.
Lines 12-14 state that polar bears' "incredible strength, as well as their thick, padded paws and razor-sharp teeth, mean that polar bears are fearsome predators on the ice".

5.   various answers possible
E.g. 'consumed' means the same as 'eaten'.

6.   D
Line 17 states that "Occasionally, polar bears can find hunting difficult if there are too few animals in the area". Therefore, it is not always easy for polar bears to find food.

7.   B
'climate' and 'predators' are nouns — they are both the names of things.

8. Seals have a lot of fat, which keeps polar bears warm.
Lines 15-16 state that a polar bear's "diet consists mainly of seals. Seals have a large amount of blubber, a thick layer of fat, which keeps the polar bear warm after it has consumed it".

9. B
Lines 18-19 state that polar bears "can sometimes travel thousands of miles alone, scouring and scavenging for food". 'scouring' and 'scavenging' mean the same as 'looking'.

Puzzles 5 — page 44

Conjunction Creek
The conjunctions are: **although**, **but**, **when**, **unless** and **or**.

River Rapids
E.g. I only go canoeing in the summer **when** the weather is hotter.
E.g. **Although** the rapids were strong, Charlotte managed to paddle.

Test 16 — pages 45-46

1. D
'broke' is correct because the sentence is in the past tense.

2. A
'furious' is correct because it makes most sense if the word following 'she would be' is an adjective — the other options are nouns or verbs.

3. C
'bought' is correct because the sentence is in the past tense and this is the only word that makes sense.

4. E
'so' is correct because it's the conjunction that makes the most sense.

5. The ba<u>k</u>ery in town makes the best pies I have ever <u>ta</u>sted. I usual<u>l</u>y buy one for myself every Saturday morning and take home a couple for my pa<u>r</u>ents.
The bits that are underlined show where a spelling mistake has been corrected. You get one mark for each of the following words you have spelt correctly: 'bakery', 'tasted', 'usually' and 'parents'.

6. B
'house's' should be 'houses' — 'houses' is a plural word and doesn't show possession, so it doesn't need an apostrophe.

7. C
The second set of speech marks should come after the question mark.

8. D
'Hall' should be 'hall' — it doesn't need a capital letter because it's a common noun, not a proper noun.

9. D
There should be speech marks after the comma.

10. D
There shouldn't be a comma after 'tickets'.

11. A
'i' should be 'I' — the pronoun 'I' is always a capital.

12. D
A question mark is needed after 'tea' instead of a comma because Marie is asking a question.

13. A
'Jacks' should be 'Jack's' — an apostrophe is needed here because the idea belongs to Jack.

Test 17 — pages 47-49

1. England
Line 1 states that "off the northeast coast of England, there is a lighthouse".

2. D
Line 1 states that the lighthouse was on "a small rocky island".

3. various answers possible
E.g. 'distress' means the same as 'danger' or 'trouble'.

4. in
'in' is a preposition because it describes a location.

5. B
Lines 8-9 state that when "daylight came, they found that a ship had been wrecked upon the rocks". Therefore, they found a ship that had crashed into the rocks.

6. A
Line 11 states that the "wind and sea were wild". 'Wild' has a similar meaning to 'fierce', so the sea could be described as fierce.

7. various answers possible
E.g. 'at once' means the same as 'straight away' or 'immediately'.

8. He was worried the boat would capsize.
Line 12 states that he "feared that the small boat would be overturned by the great waves". This suggests that he was hesitant to get in the boat because he thought it would capsize.

9. D
Line 20 states that Grace "fed" the victims of the shipwreck which means that she gave them something to eat.

Test 18 — pages 50-51

1. E
'kept' is correct because it is the correct past tense form of the verb 'to keep' which agrees with the tense of the rest of the passage.

2. C
'was' is correct because it is in the past tense and agrees with the pronoun 'it'.

3. C
'have' is correct because it completes the phrase 'would have cleaned'.

4.   D
'to' is the only word that makes sense in this sentence.

5.   "Hello, Officer," said the young man. "Do you know what the time is?"
The bits that are underlined show where punctuation has been corrected. You get one mark for each of the following: speech marks before 'Hello'; a comma after 'Officer'; speech marks after the comma after 'Officer'; and a question mark after 'is' instead of a full stop.

6.   D
'grownd' should be 'ground'.

7.   A
'Neeling' should be 'Kneeling' — there is a silent 'k'.

8.   E
'berd' should be 'bird'.

9.   D
'runing' should be 'running' — it has a double 'n'.

10.   D
'splutered' should be 'spluttered' — the word is spelt with a double 't'.

11.   B
'aword' should be 'award'.

12.   B
'epproached' should be 'approached'.

13.   C
'peace' should be 'piece'. These are homophones. 'piece' is correct because it means 'a portion of something' and 'peace' can mean 'calm'.

Puzzles 6 — page 52

PC Plod's Perplexing Cryptogram

A	B	C	D	E	F	G	H	I	J	K	L	M
5	7	22	13	9	21	8	26	20		15	1	12

N	O	P	Q	R	S	T	U	V	W	X	Y	Z
6	25	3		19	24	17	2	23	10			

A / policeman / spots / a / woman / driving / and / knitting / at / the / same / time. Driving / up / beside / her, / he / shouts... "Pull / over!"

"No," / she / shouts / back, / "a / pair / of / socks!"

Test 19 — pages 53-55

1.   various answers possible
E.g. 'taken aback' means the same as 'surprised' or 'confused'.

2.   A
Line 5 states that the gnomes "gathered for a peek". This means that they took a closer look which suggests they were curious.

3.   They are talking noisily.
'rowdy' means 'noisy' and 'chatter' means 'talk'.

4.   they
'they' refers back to the other gnomes, so it is a pronoun.

5.   C
Line 13 states that Tadfink climbed "upon a sizeable rock". 'Sizeable' means 'large' therefore it is false that Tadfink is standing on a small rock.

6.   odd
"odd" (line 16) means the same as 'strange'.

7.   saw
'saw' is an action word, so it is a verb.

8.   D
In line 23, Tadfink states that he left his "stove on". This suggests that it was because of his oven that the tree burnt down (oven is another word for stove).

9.   various answers possible
E.g. Line 23 states that Tadfink speaks "in disgust" about leaving his oven on. This suggests that he is annoyed with himself.

Test 20 — pages 56-58

1.   pianoforte
Lines 1-2 state that the pianoforte is "now simply known as the piano". This suggests that 'pianoforte' is an older name for a piano.

2.   D
Lines 1-2 state that since "the eighteenth century" the piano has been "the instrument of choice for many composers and musicians".

3.   various answers possible
E.g. 'several' means the same as 'many' or 'lots of'.

4.   C
Line 10 states that the harpsichord contains "lots of small points called 'plectra'".

5.   an
'an' is the determiner.

6.   D
Line 13 states that "Cristofori was an expert harpsichord maker". 'expert' means the same as 'skilled'.

7.   various answers possible
E.g. 'produced' means the same as 'made'.

8.   It became less popular as people started to play the piano instead.
Lines 20-21 state that "the piano gradually replaced the harpsichord, which was used a lot less frequently by the nineteenth century". This suggests that the harpsichord became less popular because of the piano.

9.   C
Line 9 states that the harpsichord "creates sound in a very different way" to the piano.

Test 21 — pages 59-60

1.   Joan shuffled towards the bal<u>c</u>ony. The s<u>c</u>ent of woodsmoke filled the air. The smell remi<u>nd</u>ed Joan of the farm, cau<u>s</u>ing her to become even more homesick.

The bits that are underlined show where a spelling mistake has been corrected. You get one mark for each of the following words you have spelt correctly: 'balcony', 'scent', 'reminded' and 'causing'.

2.   Suddenly, J<u>o</u>hn<u>'</u>s eyes grew heavy. After hauling himself onto the sofa<u>,</u> he lay down. It wasn<u>'</u>t long before he fell into a deep sleep.

The bits that are underlined show where punctuation has been corrected. You get one mark for each of the following: a capital letter at the start of 'John's'; an apostrophe in 'John's'; a comma after 'sofa'; and an apostrophe in 'wasn't'.

3.   C
'climbed' is correct because it is spelt correctly and the passage is in the past tense.

4.   E
'much' is correct because it's the only option that makes sense before the word 'higher'.

5.   D
'made' is correct because it is the correct past tense form of the verb 'to make' which agrees with the tense of the rest of the passage.

6.   A
'Looking' makes the most sense in this sentence because it describes what Jacob was doing when he 'spotted something'.

7.   B
'was' is correct because it is in the past tense and it agrees with the singular noun 'hole'.

8.   C
'could' makes the most sense in this sentence because it describes Jacob's ability to hear the tweeting sounds.

9.   E
'take' is correct because it completes the phrase 'to take a look'.

10.   C
'for' makes the most sense in this sentence.

Puzzles 7 — page 61

King Pat's Dingbats

1. think outside the box
2. full of beans
3. once in a blue moon
4. once upon a time
5. back to square one
6. on cloud nine

Test 22 — pages 62-63

1.   B
'between' is correct because it is followed by two different times.

2.   C
'should' makes the most sense in this sentence.

3.   B
'but' is the conjunction that makes the most sense.

4.   B
'worn' is correct because it is the correct past tense form of the verb 'to wear' which agrees with the tense of the rest of the passage.

5.   "You'll never bel<u>ie</u>ve what I just saw!" Joe excla<u>i</u>med from the other end of the corri<u>d</u>or. He ran towards his group of friends but tri<u>pp</u>ed over his own feet.

The bits that are underlined show where a spelling mistake has been corrected. You get one mark for each of the following words you have spelt correctly: 'believe', 'exclaimed', 'corridor' and 'tripped'.

6.   C
'july' should be 'July' — it needs a capital letter because it is a proper noun.

7.   A
There shouldn't be a comma after 'shocked'.

8.   D
'Hes' should be 'He's' — 'he's' is the shortened form of 'he is', so it needs to have an apostrophe.

9.   B
There shouldn't be a comma after 'last'.

10.   B
There should be a comma after 'guitar' to separate the adverbial from the main clause.

11.   E
'courgette's' should be 'courgettes' — 'courgettes' is a plural word and doesn't show possession, so it doesn't need an apostrophe.

12.   D
The comma after 'man' should be a question mark because the lady is asking a question.

13.   A
'miles" should be 'miles' — 'miles' is a plural word and doesn't show possession so doesn't need an apostrophe.

Test 23 — pages 64-66

1.   He is searching for gold.
Line 9 states that he is a "prospector", which is defined at the bottom of the text as someone who searches for gold. This suggests that Carson is searching for gold in the river.

2.   sweltering
"sweltering" (line 4) means the same as 'hot'.

3. A
This is a simile because the nugget is being compared to a plum by using the word 'as'.

4. various answers possible
E.g. a story which might be made up.

5. various answers possible
His parents are not happy about him being a prospector. Line 9 states that his parents "had never fully supported his decision to become a prospector" which suggests they are not happy about it.

6. B
Lines 11-12 state that "a papery moon hung in the sky", which suggests that it's getting dark.

7. B
'immediately' is an adverb because it describes the verb 'pulling'.

8. various answers possible
E.g. Carson has found some gold and doesn't want anyone else to know. In line 19, he finds something that is "unmistakably gold". In line 23, he tells another man that what he found was just "a piece of glass catchin' the sun". This suggests that he doesn't want anyone to know that he's found gold. Therefore, he moves calmly to try to hide the fact that he has found gold.

9. A
Line 10 states that "he was desperate" to make his parents proud. This suggests that he does care what his family thinks.

Test 24 — pages 67-68

1. E
'spent' is correct because it is the correct past tense form of the verb 'to spend'.

2. A
'have' is correct because it completes the phrase 'should have been'.

3. E
'snowed' is correct because it agrees with the tense of the passage and is the only word that makes sense.

4. D
'were' is correct because it is a verb which agrees with the plural noun 'lessons'.

5. All morning, Richard had been baking a cake for his wife. He wasn't a very good baker, so he called her down for help. She was furious that she had to help.
The bits that are underlined show where punctuation has been corrected. You get one mark for each of the following: a comma after 'morning'; an apostrophe in 'wasn't'; no speech marks before 'down'; and no speech marks after 'help'.

6. D
'gotes' should be 'goats'.

7. D
'protecsion' should be 'protection' — the correct suffix is 'tion'.

8. A
'pursonal' should be 'personal'.

9. C
'cerial' should be 'cereal' — the ending is 'eal'.

10. A
'tyrelessly' should be 'tirelessly' — the root word is 'tire', as in 'tired'.

11. B
'pare' should be 'pair'.

12. D
'examening' should be 'examining'.

13. E
'behavour' should be 'behaviour' — the correct suffix is '-iour'.

Puzzles 8 — page 69

The Word Factory

Dear Ronald,
          I am writing to **warn** you. You must not **explore** the caves with Donald. This is very **important**. I have reason to believe he is **dangerous**. He is working with the man-eating cave troll, luring people into his cave so that the troll can eat them. **Meet** me outside the caves instead and I will make sure you are **safe**.
          Yours sincerely, Clive Trole

Test 25 — pages 70-72

1. various answers possible
E.g. They gather round anyone who has food. Lines 1-2 ask "Have you ever been at the British seaside and found yourself surrounded by greedy seagulls as soon as you start tucking into your fish and chips?" This suggests that the author is describing the animals as 'greedy' because they gather round anyone who has food.

2. C
'pesky pigeon pecking' is alliteration because all three words begin with 'p'.

3. It's not only animals in the UK that loiter round humans to try to get food but animals all over the world.
'particular to' means 'unique to', so the sentence suggests that loitering near humans is not something only animals in the UK do.

4. because they like to eat tourists' food
Lines 7-8 state that macaques "often congregate near tourist attractions because they know that they can stuff themselves silly on scraps from visitors". This suggests that they go near tourist attractions because they know there will be a lot of people there who will give them food.

5. He's the leader of a troop of monkeys who bring food to him.
Lines 13-14 state that, because "he's the leader of a troop of monkeys, the other members of the troop scavenge for him and bring Uncle Fat the choicest leftovers".

6.   amusing
"amusing" (line 15) means the same as 'funny'.

7.   To help him lose weight and improve his health
Lines 15-16 state that "conservation groups became worried about Uncle Fat's health", and line 18 states that he's been "put on a strict diet" in a rehabilitation centre "in an attempt to help him shed some weight".

8.   A
'extreme' and 'exceptional' both mean 'unusual'.

9.   D
Line 21 states that some people are concerned that if macaques become dependent on the food humans give them then "they'll forget how to hunt for themselves".

Test 26 — pages 73-74

1.   The photographer pointed her camera towards the celebrities walking down the red carpet. She pressed the button, hoping to get a good shot.
The bits that are underlined show where a spelling mistake has been corrected. You get one mark for each of the following words you have spelt correctly: 'photographer', 'carpet', 'pressed' and 'button'.

2.   It's believed that fireworks were invented in China in the seventh century. However, fireworks wouldn't become popular in Europe for another thousand years.
The bits that are underlined show where punctuation has been corrected. You get one mark for each of the following: an apostrophe in 'It's'; a capital letter at the start of 'China'; a lower-case letter at the start of 'century'; and an apostrophe in 'wouldn't'.

3.   B
'in' makes the most sense in this sentence.

4.   C
'told' is correct because it is the correct past tense form of the verb 'to tell' which agrees with the tense of the rest of the passage.

5.   E
'took' is correct because it is the correct past tense form of the verb 'to take' which agrees with the tense of the rest of the passage.

6.   A
'brought' is correct because it is the correct past tense form of the verb 'to bring' which agrees with the tense of the rest of the passage.

7.   E
'do' is the only word that makes sense in this sentence,

8.   A
'lying' is correct because it is the only word that makes sense in this sentence.

9.   E
'their' is correct because it agrees with the plural 'lions' and shows that the nap belongs to them.

10.   E
'behind' makes the most sense in this sentence.

Test 27 — pages 75-77

1.   D
Line 1 states that the Peppery Man is "thin". 'Thin' means the same as 'slim'.

2.   B
Line 3 states that he "shook his fist" and "his hair he tore". Line 4 states that he "slammed the door". It is never mentioned that he complains to his neighbours.

3.   yelled
"yelled" (line 12) means the same as 'shouted'.

4.   D
'frown' is a facial expression, so it is a noun because it is a name of a thing.

5.   preposition
'over' is a preposition because it describes where the Peppery Man is scolding.

6.   The neighbours know he is angry when he roars.
Lines 17-18 state that "His neighbours, when they hear his roars, / Closed their blinds and locked their doors". This suggests that it is his roars that tell them he's angry.

7.   They hide and try to get away from the noise.
Lines 18-20 state that his neighbours "Closed their blinds and locked their doors, / Shut their windows, sought their beds, / Stopped their ears and covered their heads".

8.   taken over by extreme anger
'fiery rage' means 'extreme anger' and 'consumed' can mean 'taken over by something', so the Peppery Man is taken over by extreme anger.

9.   B
Lines 23-24 state "And no one knew, when he was vexed, / What in the world would happen next" . This suggests that the Peppery Man is unpredictable when he is angry.

Puzzles 9 — page 78

Homnomnoms

leak — leek
stake — steak
been — bean
bury — berry
pair — pear
flower — flour

Test 28 — pages 79-80

1.   C
'couldn't' makes the most sense in the context of the passage.

2. B
'in' makes the most sense in this sentence.

3. C
'ran' is correct because it is the correct past tense form of the verb 'to run'.

4. D
'within' makes the most sense in this sentence.

5. The weather had been beautiful all day and Sophia had been relaxing on the beach. She went for a swim in the sea, but it was freezing cold. She couldn't stop shivering.
The bits that are underlined show where a spelling mistake has been corrected. You get one mark for each of the following words you have spelt correctly: 'weather', 'beautiful', 'sea' and 'shivering'.

6. A
'Lucys' should be 'Lucy's' — an apostrophe is needed here because the parents belong to Lucy.

7. E
'wouldnt' should be 'wouldn't'. This is a shortened version of 'would not', and the apostrophe replaces the missing letter 'o'.

8. D
There should be a comma between 'flour' and 'eggs' to separate the items in the list.

9. D
There should be speech marks after the question mark.

10. B
A question mark is needed after 'tonight' instead of a comma because Rachel is asking a question.

11. D
There should be a full stop after Thursday to mark the end of the sentence.

12. C
There shouldn't be a comma after 'capital'.

13. B
'whos' should be 'who's' — 'who's' is the shortened form of 'who is', so it needs to have an apostrophe.

Test 29 — pages 81-82

1. D
'forward' is correct because it completes the phrase 'looking forward to', which makes the most sense in this sentence.

2. C
'had' is correct because the passage is in the past tense, and it completes the phrase 'he had made'.

3. D
'went' is correct because it is the past tense form of 'to go' which agrees with the rest of the passage.

4. D
'led' is correct because it is the correct past tense form of the verb 'to lead' which agrees with the tense of the passage.

5. "Aah!" shrieked Harry as a mouse ran across the kitchen. He jumped on a chair and refused to come down. The mouse saw he was scared and went about his business as slowly as possible.
The bits that are underlined show where punctuation has been corrected. You get one mark for each of the following: speech marks after the exclamation mark; a lower-case letter at the start of 'shrieked'; a full stop after 'down' and no apostrophe at the end of 'business'.

6. C
'iland' should be 'island' — the 's' is silent.

7. B
'adress' should be 'address' — it has a double 'd'.

8. E
'dissapeared' should be 'disappeared' — the prefix is 'dis' and the root word is 'appear'.

9. B
'intrested' should be 'interested' — the root word is 'interest'.

10. C
'where' should be 'were'.

11. B
'brout' should be 'brought'.

12. B
'poplar' should be 'popular'.

13. E
'rinkly' should be 'wrinkly' — the 'w' is silent.

Test 30 — pages 83-85

1. because it is a large swampy area that flows like a river
Line 6 states that the Everglades is actually a "very large and slow-moving river". Line 5 states that it is "often thought to be a large swamp or marsh" — these are places where grasses and other plants grow. This suggests that it is called the "River of Grass" because it is a large river with lots of grass.

2. B
Lines 8-9 state that the Everglades's "tropical climate means that its wildlife is very different to elsewhere in North America". Therefore, it is because of its tropical climate that the Everglades is home to species not found elsewhere in North America.

3. prowl
"prowl" (line 10) means the same as 'stalk'.

4. C
Lines 11-13 state that crocodiles "can be told apart from alligators by their V-shaped snout, which differs from the alligator's more rounded nose". This means that they have different shaped snouts.

5. adjective
'fearsome' is an adjective because it describes the noun 'predators'.

6.   C
Lines 14-15 state that "more people in the US are killed by cows than by alligators and crocodiles". Manatees are described as a "gentler animal" (line 16) which suggests that they are less harmful than alligators and crocodiles.

7.   They are similar to cows, but they live in the water.
Line 17 states that manatees are "large, slow-moving mammals" that graze "on seagrass". Cows are large, slow-moving mammals that graze on grass. Therefore, manatees are called 'sea cows' because they are similar to cows, but they live in the water.

8.   D
'estimated' and 'guessed' both mean 'gave a rough answer without knowing if it is correct'.

9.   Florida panther
Line 20 states that the Florida panther lives "in the forests around the wetlands". Therefore, it lives in the Everglades but not in the water.

Puzzles 10 — page 86

Treasure Hunt Tricks
Claude spells 'restaraunt' incorrectly. It should be **restaurant**. He is lying, which rules out E.
Jill doesn't spell anything incorrectly, so she is telling the truth. This rules out D.
Philippa spells 'cathedrel' incorrectly. It should be **cathedral**. She is lying, which means the treasure is near the cathedral.
Karl spells 'rite' incorrectly. It should be **right**. He is lying, which rules out A.
Urslan spells 'betwen' incorrectly. It should be **between**. He is lying, which rules out B.

So the treasure is at location **C** — A, B, D and E have been ruled out.

Test 31 — pages 87-88

1.   Martin had spent all night on his hi<u>s</u>tory homework. He was doing a project on the Tudors, but he found doing his own rese<u>a</u>rch quite diffi<u>c</u>ult. His dad had been too b<u>u</u>sy to give him any help.
The bits that are underlined show where a spelling mistake has been corrected. You get one mark for each of the following words you have spelt correctly: 'history', 'research', 'difficult' and 'busy'.

2.   Wendy'<u>s</u> sister is having a birthday party on <u>S</u>aturday. <u>A</u>lthough Wendy had tried to bake her a cake<u>,</u> she had burnt it and had to buy one instead.
The bits that are underlined show where punctuation has been corrected. You get one mark for each of the following: an apostrophe in 'Wendy's'; a capital letter at the start of 'Saturday'; a capital letter at the start of 'Although'; and a comma after 'cake'.

3.   A
'dropped' is correct because the passage is in the past tense.

4.   E
'Patting' is correct because it makes the most sense in the sentence.

5.   B
'forgotten' is correct because it is the correct past tense form of the verb 'to forget'.

6.   E
'leaves' makes the most sense in the sentence because it's describing something that is going to happen in the future.

7.   C
'began' is correct because it is in the past tense.

8.   C
'see' is correct because it makes the most sense in this sentence.

9.   E
'shouting' is correct because it completes the phrase "They were shouting".

10.   B
'put' is correct because it is in the past tense and it makes the most sense in this sentence.

Test 32 — pages 89-91

1.   D
Lines 1-2 state that "he assumed it was just a crack of thunder".

2.   A
Lines 5-6 state that "His irritation suddenly turned to curiosity". Therefore, he was irritated when he went to open the curtains which means he can be described as annoyed.

3.   various answers possible
E.g. 'hectically' means the same as 'frantically' or 'excitedly'.

4.   quickly
'quickly' is an adverb because it describes the verb 'chattering'.

5.   various answers possible
E.g. Will is not scared. He is keen to find out more about the creatures. Line 13 states that he is "not easily frightened", and line 14 states that he is "fascinated by his strange visitors".

6.   C
This is a simile because his movements are being compared to a mouse by using the word 'as'.

7.   B
Lines 14-15 state that Will moved quietly, "not wanting to spook the mysterious creatures", meaning that he didn't want to scare them.

8.   C
Line 17 states that Will "walked into a tree and hit his head". This suggests that the reason he is asleep in the garden is because he passed out from hitting his head on the tree.

9. She wouldn't have believed it.
Line 20 states that Will didn't tell his mother the truth because there's "no way she would have believed it".

Test 33 — pages 92-94

1. various answers possible
E.g. they had "bright green skin" (line 4); they "wore strange clothes" (line 5); they were "noticeably starved" (line 5).

2. adjective
'unknown' is an adjective because it's used to describe the noun 'language'.

3. A
'noticeably' and 'clearly' both mean 'obviously'.

4. various answers possible
E.g. The children looked starved, so it's strange that they only wanted to eat broad beans.

5. C
Lines 11-12 state that the children "had been looking after their father's cattle when they followed the animals into a cave. They then followed the sound of bells and came out on the other side at Woolpit".

6. various answers possible
Line 10 states that "the sun never shone in St. Martin's Land". This suggests that they were not used to the sunlight, so they found it startling.

7. D
Line 15 states that some people think the story is "a local folk legend made up by the villagers". Line 17 states that some people think they were "orphans from Belgium". Line 16 states that some people think they were "aliens". There is no mention of a prank.

8. C
Line 19 states that, according to the rational explanation, their green skin was "due to a very poor diet".

9. various answers possible
E.g. 'fascinate' means the same at 'interest' or 'captivate'.

16